For C

THE M1 GARAND 1936 TO 1957

JOE POYER
CRAIG RIESCH

EDITED BY

SIMEON STODDARD
CURATOR, RET., CODY FIREARMS MUSEUM

4TH EDITION, REVISED AND EXPANDED

North Cape Publications®, Inc.

For all the veterans of World War II, Korea and Post-World War II conflicts who carried—and depended on—John C. Garand's great battle rifle, as they made it safe for all of us to live our lives as we see fit.

The authors wish to thank those who helped in preparing this text, especially Ken Fladrich and Mike Metzgar of The Armory of Orange, Orange, California, Scott Duff for information and encouragement, and John Capalbo, John Jordan and Woody Travis for making available M1 Garands and accessories from their collections. Most particularly would we like to thank Howard Michael Madaus and Simeon Stoddard, past curators of the Cody Firearms Museum, Buffalo Bill Historical Center, Cody, Wyoming, for all their time and wonderful cooperation in allowing us access to their fine collections. Our thanks also to Thomas J. Bond; CDR Chris Sullivan, USNR; Raymond G. Loynes; Don Woolridge; Jerry Woolf; and Warren Yakey for their generous assistance in revising this and past editions. Any errors are solely the responsibility of the authors.

This publication is designed to provide authoritative and accurate information in regard to the subject matter covered. However, it should be recognized that serial numbers and dates, as well as other information given within, are necessarily limited by the accuracy of the source materials.

ISBN 1-882391-19-5
North Cape Publications®, Inc., P.O. Box 1027,
Tustin, California 92781
Phone: 800 745-9714; Fax: 714 832-5302.
E-mail: ncape@ix.netcom.com; Website: www.northcapepubs.com
Printed in the USA by Delta Printing Solutions, Valencia, CA 91355

Table of Contents

Introduction 1
CHAPTER 1 THE M1 GARAND RIFLE 2
John C. Garand 2
The Garand Is Adopted 3
Ironing Out the Bugs 5
NRA Questions 5
First Combat in the Philippines! 6
European Mud and Snow 7
The M1 Garand in the Cold War 7
Drawing Numbers 8
Manufacturer's Markings 9
Proof Marks 10
Heat Treatment Lot Numbers 10
Conventions 11
Exploded View, M1 Garand 20

CHAPTER 2 THE M1 GARAND, PART-BY-PART 23
RECEIVER 24
Physical Characteristics 24
Differentiating Between Manufacturers of
M1 Garand Receivers 26
Receiver Material 26
Determining If a Receiver Has Been Demilitarized 30
Clip Latch Assembly 31
Clip Latch 32
Clip Latch Spring 33
Clip Latch Pin 33
Rear Sight Assembly 34
Rear Sight Base 44
Aperture 45
Rear Sight Cover 47
BOLT 49
Bolt Body 49
Extractor 51

The M1 Garand

Extractor Spring and Plunger Assembly 54
Ejector 54
Ejector Spring 55
Firing Pin 56
BARRELS 57
Barrel Dimensions 57
Barrel Markings 60
Barrel Finish 64
Barrel Rifling 65
OPERATING ROD ASSEMBLY 67
Operating Rod 67
Operating Rod Spring 73
Compensating Spring 74
Follower Rod Assembly 74
Operating Rod Catch Assembly 75
Operating Rod Catch 78
Accelerator 79
Accelerator Rivet 80
Follower Arm 80
Follower Arm Pin 82
Follower 82
Bullet Guide 84
TRIGGER ASSEMBLY 87
Trigger Housing 87
Trigger Guard 91
Trigger/Sear Assembly 93
Trigger Pin 95
Sear Pin 95
Hammers 96
Hammer Spring Plunger 99
Hammer Spring 100
Hammer Spring Housing 101
Safety 101
Ejector Clip 102
Hammer Pin 103

The M1 Garand

GAS CYLINDER ASSEMBLY 105
   Gas Cylinder, Type 1 (Gas Trap M1) 106
   Gas Cylinder, Type 2 (Gas Port M1) 107
     Front Sight Base Modifications................................ 108
     Gas Cylinder Plug 111
     Gas Cylinder Lock 112
     Gas Cylinder Lock Screw 113
   Front Sight Assembly 116
     Front Sight.. 116
     Front Sight Screw 118
     Front Sight Screw Seal 119
   Stacking Swivel Assembly... 119
     Stacking Swivel 119
     Stacking Swivel Screw... 120
STOCKS 121
   Type 1 M1 Garand Stocks.. 121
   Type 2 M1 Garand Stocks 123
   Type 3 M1 Garand Stock.. 124
   Type 4 M1 Garand Stock.. 124
   Type 5 M1 Garand Stock.. 124
   Winchester Stocks—Notes 125
   International Harvester M1 Garand Stocks—Notes 128
   Harrington & Richardson M1 Garand Stocks—Notes 129
     Inspection Cartouche.. 129
     Ordnance Department Cartouche 131
     Proof Firing Cartouche 132
     Clean and Repair Program 133
   Stock Ferrule 140
     Stock Ferrule Swivel.. 142
     Stock Ferrule Swivel Screw 142
BUTT PLATE ASSEMBLY 143
   Butt Swivel 144
   Butt Swivel Screw 145
HANDGUARD ASSEMBLIES... 148
   Front Handguard 148

The M1 Garand

Front Handguard Liner 149
Front Handguard Ferrule.. 150
Rear Handguard 151
Rear Handguard Band 152
Lower Band 153
Lower Band Retaining Pin 155

CHAPTER 3 M1 GARAND TOOLS,
AMMUNITION AND ACCESSORIES 156
Oiler.. 156
Pull-Through and Bore Brush...................................... 157
Brush, Cleaning 158
Grease Pot.. 158
Combination Tool... 158
Post-Korean War Cleaning Kit 161
Ammunition... 162
M1 Garand Rifle En-Bloc Clips 165
M1 Garand Slings... 166
Model 1907 Sling, Type 1 166
Model 1907 Sling, Type 2 166
Model 1923 Sling, Type 1 167
Model 1923 Sling, Type 2 167
M1 Sling, Improved.. 167
M1 Garand Rifle Blank Firing Attachment.................... 168
Bayonets 169
Model 1905 Bayonet, Type 1 169
Model 1905 Bayonet, Type 2.................................... 170
Bayonet, M1.. 171
Model 1905E1 Bayonet.. 171
Bayonet, M5.. 172
Modified Scabbards 173
Ruptured Case Extractor.. 173
Muzzle Cover.. 174
Barrel Reflectors 174
Cartridge Belts and Pouches 175

The M1 Garand

M1 Garand Ammunition Pouch 177
   Pouch, Ammunition, Universal 177
   Bandolier 178
   Grenade Launcher 179
  Dummy Rifle Grenades 180

Appendix A: M1 Garand Serial Numbers 182

Appendix B: M1 Garand Sniper Rifles 186

Appendix C: National Match M1 Garand Rifles 201

Appendix D: U.S. Navy and Other 7.62 X 51 mm M1 Garands 208

Appendix E: British M1 Garands 212

Appendix F: Danish M1 Garands 215

Appendix G: Disassembly, Assembly, Cleaning
  and Maintenance of the M1 Rifle 223

Appendix H: The Importance of Barrel Gauges 229

Appendix I: Attaching the Model 1907 Leather Sling 232

Appendix J: Glossary 236

Appendix K: Bibliography 240

Aids for Collectors 245
About the Authors and Editor 246
Books from North Cape Publications®, Inc. 248
M1 Garand Evaluation Sheet 254

The M1 Garand

INTRODUCTION

The M1 Garand was described by no less an authority than General George S. Patton, Jr., as "the greatest battle implement ever devised." Most combat infantrymen who carried and used the M1 Garand during World War II and Korea, and many lesser military actions between and after, would agree with him wholeheartedly.

The M1 Garand battle rifle provided the combat infantryman with the best combat arm in two major wars and innumerable smaller ones. A total of 4,040,802 M1 Garands were placed in the hands of American fighting men during World War II. During and after the Korean War, another 1,427,970 M1s were manufactured for a total production of 5,468,772 rifles. Nearly 74% of that total—and the entire production for World War II—were produced at the Springfield National Armory and at the Winchester Repeating Arms Company. In the postwar years, production at International Harvester and Harrington & Richardson supplemented the reopened manufacturing and assembly lines at the Springfield Armory.

The M1 Garand was one of those weapon systems that the media and politicians loved to deride. However, not a single dire prediction made by any critic of the rifle or its performance ever came true. The M1 Garand earned a well-deserved reputation as one of the most reliable military firearms ever developed.

In the four decades of its service life, the M1 Garand was subjected to the numerous changes, official as well as unofficial, which occur when a rifle is long in military service. Parts were interchanged with other rifles, stocks were broken and replaced, sanded and refinished, and metal was re-Parkerized or else coated with a black oxide finish. In foreign military service, similar changes occurred and parts were even replaced with those of local manufacture.

The books in the "For Collectors Only" series are written and organized to provide the collector with a part-by-part by serial number range analysis of a firearm. This format aids the collector who demands a firearm that is as close to "original issue" as possible. With spare parts widely available, plus this book, most M1 Garands can be restored to original or near-original condition. Best of luck!

The M1 Garand

CHAPTER 1
THE M1 GARAND RIFLE

After World War I ended in November 1918, military planners in many nations studied the effectiveness of bolt-action repeating rifles during the period 1914-1918. Most came to the same conclusions, that 1) future wars would involve movement and maneuverability and 2) massed small-arms fire would play a critical part in fighting and winning those wars. Nearly all military planners made the same recommendation to their national governments: develop a semiautomatic infantry rifle.

But in only two nations were those recommendations taken seriously, and interestingly enough, both nations had rejected war as a means for settling international differences after the terrible bloodletting of World War I. In the United States of America and the Union of Soviet Socialist Republics, funds were made available—however paltry—and orders were given to develop a semiautomatic infantry rifle for general issue.

John C. Garand

The experience of the United States military with semiautomatic or selective fire individual combat infantry weapons, scarce as it was, was exceeded only by that of Germany. During World War I, the Browning Automatic Rifle and the Pedersen Device for the Model 1903 Springfield Rifle had been developed, but the BAR only saw action in the last month and the Pedersen Device was not intended for use until the 1919 offensives. In spite of a national government bent on withdrawing into international isolation, a severely reduced military budget and internal squabbling, the U.S. Army forged ahead as fast as limited funding and manpower allowed.

The first tests for a new semiautomatic rifle were conducted in 1921. Dozens of designs were submitted and tested to eliminate those not suitable for military service. A complete discussion of this process is beyond the scope of this essay but can be found in

The M1 Garand

Major General Julian Hatcher's *Book of the Garand*. See Appendix K, Bibliography.

One of the leading candidate designs was that of John Cantius Garand (rhymes with errand). Garand, a general ordnance design engineer at the Springfield Armory, submitted a prototype rifle which used the cartridge primer to drive back the firing pin which in turn opened the bolt and extracted the spent cartridge case. His new rifle required a special .276 cartridge. Garand resubmitted the rifle design in 1922 and again in 1926, each time with improvements that increased the rifle's reliability and decreased potential manufacturing costs. The Army was unwilling to change to a new cartridge but as Garand's rifle appeared promising, he was asked to redesign it using the standard-issue .30-06 cartridge and a gas-actuated mechanism with the gas being supplied by the burning propellant.

In 1929, Garand submitted the new rifle design. He had built two prototypes, one in .30-06 caliber and the other for the then-experimental .276-caliber cartridge, but had submitted only the .276-caliber rifle for testing. The new design employed a spring-loaded piston/operating rod to open the bolt and eject the cartridge, rather than the rearward movement of the cartridge's primer. A gas cylinder was mounted at the end of the barrel and a portion of the expanding gases bled into it where they continued to expand, thus moving the piston to the rear. The piston/operating rod was connected to an ear on the bolt and the rearward movement of the "operating rod" against the bolt ear caused it to open as it traveled backward in its track. As the bolt moved backward, it compressed a spring contained in the tubular operating rod. When the bolt reached the end of its track, the spring drove it forward to strip a new cartridge from the magazine and drive it into the breech, then lock the bolt shut, ready to fire.

The Garand Is Adopted

The 1929 trial pitted Garand's "T3" design against, among others, the "T1" dropping block action developed by John D. Pedersen. Garand's design was found to be superior and easier to produce. Suggestions were made for further improvements and twenty rifles

The M1 Garand

designated T3E2 were built for further testing. A second design, the T1E1, was completed and tested in 1931. The following year, the decision was made by the U.S. Army to retain the .30-06 as the standard service cartridge and all further development work on Garand's semiautomatic cartridge and rifle was halted; temporarily, as it turned out.

In March 1932, the Board on Semiautomatic Rifles ordered the manufacture of seventy-seven T1E1 .30-caliber rifles for additional service tests at Springfield Armory under the designation T1E2. A few weeks later, the designation was changed to U.S. Rifle Semiautomatic, Caliber .30, M1. The new M1 rifles were completed by August 1934, along with tooling, fixtures and gauges. Testing was completed by the end of August the following year and a strong recommendation was made for the adoption of the M1 rifle. The new rifle was standardized (adopted) on January 9, 1936, as U.S. Semiautomatic Rifle, Caliber .30, M1. The Armed Services referred to it as the "M1 Rifle" but collectors refer to it as the M1 Garand, or simply, as the "Garand," out of respect for the inventor.

In the years between adoption and the American involvement in World War II, the M1 underwent extended testing. The hand-built tool-room models performed as expected but annoying problems cropped up in production models. Almost all were traced to the changes introduced in dimensions and shapes during the transition to production tooling. John C. Garand, the designer of the rifle, had not been consulted in the tooling preparation, even though he had designed each part with two objectives in mind—reliability and ease of manufacturing.

According to Major General Julian Hatcher—who was present at the Springfield Armory in those days—one "officer of high rank gravely recommended that in view of the shortage of appropriations, he (Garand) be dropped from the payroll to save his $3,500 (annual) salary." The officer's suggestion was greeted with outrage and Garand was not only retained but brought back into the research process.

The M1 Garand

Ironing Out the Bugs

Five major problems with the new M1 Garand were identified: 1) seventh-round stoppage, 2) clips that jumped from the breech containing the last round, 3) sticking operating rod cams, 4) problems with the rear sight and 5) the gas trap design.

The first four problems were solved with only minor changes to the design of the tooling. But the last required a significant redesign. The gas trap system allowed gas to flow between the end of the muzzle and the gas trap assembly. It was difficult to clean, and the carbon deposits which quickly built up limited the amount of gas available to drive the operating rod and also interfered with accuracy. And because the gas cylinder assembly was attached to the muzzle, it did not form a strong mounting for the bayonet.

Garand's solution was to substitute a gas port or vent 0.0805 inch in diameter in the barrel proper. The gas which flowed through the port moved at such a high velocity that carbon could not build up. In effect, the gas port was self-cleaning. A new gas cylinder was also developed and the barrel was lengthened to 24 inches. The new gas port for the M1 Garand was adopted on October 26, 1939, and production was changed from the gas trap to the gas port at circa serial #50,000—July 1940.

NRA Questions

The next challenge to the M1 Garand came from an unexpected quarter in 1939, at the National Matches. National Rifle Association marksmen were not happy with the M1 Garand. They contrasted its appearance with that of the sleek, finely honed Model 1903A1 National Match Rifle and found its bulky silhouette and wobbly front sight wanting. They compared the vernier rear sight on the M1903 with the wide aperture sight on the M1 Garand and were convinced the sight was substandard. They were especially unhappy with the front sight which was mounted on the end of the gas cylinder (this was the gas trap model) and which tended to move. The Army tried its best to gloss over what they saw as uninformed criticism. But NRA staff members—most of them World War I veterans—began asking pointed questions about the rifle.

The M1 Garand

The Army made no special effort to address their concerns, even as those corrections were being made to the rifle.

In April 1940, an editorial in the *American Rifleman* demanded answers about the M1 Garand and its suitability as a military rifle. The reverberations reached all the way to Congress, which threatened to eliminate appropriations for the new rifle. The threat finally got the Army's attention. One particularly effective criticism of the Army's battle-rifle development project had concerned the supposed haste with which the Johnson Semiautomatic rifle had been eliminated from consideration. The Army arranged a public demonstration of both rifles at Fort Belvoir, Virginia, and it was well attended by representatives from both houses of Congress, and from the NRA. The M1 Garand performed as designed. Senator Ernest Lundeen shot 27 successive bull's-eyes at 300 yards.

In November 1940, the Marine Corps completed its own set of tests and concluded that the M1 Garand "is the most satisfactory semiautomatic rifle available." With Congress and the NRA now convinced, the Army was allowed to continue tooling up both the Springfield National Armory and Winchester Repeating Arms Company for wartime production.

Winchester encountered a few difficulties in tooling, but its first production rifles were gas port rifles completed on January 10, 1941, the same day that Springfield reached a production figure of 600 rifles per day. Regular production at Winchester was preceded by a series of "educational rifles" to prove the tooling. These rifles exhibit some characteristics of the gas trap rifles as they were built according to drawings primarily dated August 2, 1937, of the gas trap model. Monthly production at Springfield and Winchester ultimately reached highs of 122,001 in January 1944 and 16,000 in October 1943, respectively.

First Combat in the Philippines!
The M1 Garand's first real combat test came during the battle for the Philippines in early 1942. Only a few reports concerning the rifle's effectiveness under battle conditions filtered out from the besieged garrisons, but those few were extremely positive. Later that year, Marines equipped with the M1903 bolt-action rifle land-

The M1 Garand

ed on Guadalcanal. Army troops landed to support them carried the new M1 Garand. The Marine Corps, which had been reluctant to give up their M1903s, received a first-hand lesson in superior firepower and before long, every Marine on the island was begging, borrowing or stealing Garands from the Army.

Troops who used the new rifle in the South Pacific were astonished at how well it stood up to the salt-water corrosion, the sand, mud, tropical rain—or, in the Aleutians—to the freezing fogs and snow. The quick-detachable stock made it easy for troops to clean the rifle, whether they were in trenches, foxholes, the crowded confines of troop ships or in rear-area quarters.

European Mud and Snow
In the European theater, the M1 Garand's first battle test came in North Africa. Soldiers waded ashore against heavy resistance in some areas and no resistance in others. In either case, the M1 Garand ignored salt-water dunkings and beach sand. As the troops moved inland into the desert areas, the new rifle continued to function reliably in spite of blowing sand after troops learned to wipe off lubrication. From Sicily to Normandy, from the English Channel to the Elbe, the M1 Garand became the soldier's best friend. The semiautomatic fire mode gave the American soldier a definite advantage over Axis troops, armed for the most part with bolt-action rifles.

The M1 Garand served again during the Korean campaign, once more providing the American soldier a definite edge over the North Korean and Chinese troops armed with obsolete World War II bolt-action rifles, submachine guns of Russian design and a very few of the Russian-designed semiautomatic SKS carbines.

The M1 Garand in the Cold War
The M1 Garand was distributed widely to American allies and friends around the world as the Cold War heated up. The Italian Army rearmed with the Garand. Republic of Korea troops carried the M1 Garand long after the Armistice was signed on July 27, 1953. French troops armed with the M1 Garand fought Viet Minh troops during the first war in Vietnam. And when the U.S. Army

The M1 Garand

replaced the M1 Garand in 1957, it was with the M14 battle rifle, a derivative of John C. Garand's famous development.

For twenty years, the M1 Garand served as the first-line personal combat rifle of American troops, and served well and proudly all around the world.

Table 1 Specifications, U.S. Rifle, Caliber .30, M1	
Weight	9.5 pounds
Weight with bayonet, rifle and sling M1907	11.2 pounds
Length (overall) rifle only	43.6 inches
Length of barrel	24 inches
Weight of barrel	2.58 pounds
Length of rifling	21-30 inches; 70.8 calibers
Number of grooves	4
Right-hand twist	1:10 inches
Depth of grooves	0.0040 inch
Cross-sectional area of bore	0.0740 square inch
Type of mechanism	gas-operated, semiautomatic
Loading device	en-bloc clip, 8 rounds
Rate of fire	Semiautomatic
Cooling	Air
Sight radius	27.9 inches at l00-yard range
Normal pressure	50,000 pounds per square inch
Ammunition	Cal. .30, M2

Drawing Numbers

Each part of the M1 Garand was assigned an engineering drawing number. These controlled drawings followed a specific set of standards to make certain that all parts were completely interchangeable, met specific quality-control objectives and to assure that the latest authorized drawing was always in use. The drawing number was also used as the part number until the end of the Korean War. Drawing numbers were then incorporated into the eleven-digit

The M1 Garand

Federal Stock Number system, which was in turn superseded by the fourteen-digit National Stock Number system. In both cases, the letter prefix was dropped and the number, without hyphens, was incorporated.

Four sizes of drawing sheets were used, designated by the letters A (8.5 x 11 inches), B (11 x 17 inches), C (17 x 22 inches) and D (22 x 34 inches). These letters also form the prefix to the drawing or part number. The major parts of the M1 Garand were stamped with the drawing number and any revision to that drawing. They include the receiver, bolt, barrel, safety and trigger guard housing, operating rod and hammer. Other parts were stamped with their drawing number during early production to circa serial #28,000, after which the practice was restricted only to major parts.

Manufacturer's Markings
This brief overview will introduce the collector to the markings found on M1 Garand parts. They will be discussed in detail in the section describing each part.

Barrels, receivers, bolts, trigger housings, triggers, hammers, safeties, operating rods, early stocks, sight knobs and Type 2 gas plugs were marked by the manufacturer. Commonly seen designations or abbreviations on barrels and some other parts are SA=Springfield Armory; WRA, W, A, CM or punch mark=Winchester; IHC=International Harvester; HRA=Harrington & Richardson Arms; and in the case of barrels, LMR=Line Material Company, on barrels manufactured for International Harvester. "MARLIN" barrels were replacements.

Other parts can sometimes be identified as Winchester-manufacture by a rougher finish than applied to Springfield rifles. Winchester parts can also be identified by the presence of a punch mark thought by some to test hardness but more likely was used to indicate that the part had been inspected and passed. This is not a foolproof method of identifying Winchester parts as hardness-test punch marks also appear on non-Winchester-manufactured parts. Various letters and numbers will be found on other parts and are assumed to be inspectors at the major contractors' plants, or those

The M1 Garand

of subcontractors. During rebuild periods at U.S. military facilities and foreign rebuild facilities, inspection marks were sometimes stamped on stocks but infrequently on metal parts.

Proof Marks
Two proof marks were stamped on M1 Garands: 1) the barrel proof mark was a "P" stamped on the top, and later on the right side of the barrel where it was visible when the operating slide was drawn to the rear; 2) the "P" or "P" proof mark was stamped on the forward surface of the pistol grip.

Each M1 Garand was submitted to two firing tests. The first consisted of a proof-firing with a 70,000 psi cartridge. After firing, both the rifle and the spent cartridge case were examined for any signs of bulging, cracking, splitting, ringing or other problems. If the rifle passed, the barrel and stock wrist were proof marked. The second test was for function and accuracy and consisted of twenty-four rounds. The rifle was rejected for any malfunction, or if it couldn't be zeroed, and sent back for repair.

Final Acceptance Cartouche
The inspector's final cartouche with the initials of the manufacturer and the inspector was contained within a rectangle stamped on the left side of the stock above the trigger assembly. The initials of the manufacturer (with periods) were placed above the initials of the inspector, i.e., S.A./G.A.W. for Springfield Armory/George A. Woody.

Beginning in September-October 1953, a generic cartouche consisting of an eagle with upraised wings under three stars, contained within a box with rounded corners, replaced the previous style of cartouche. It was stamped on the left side of the stock, above the trigger assembly. The new cartouche was officially the "Defense Acceptance stamp," but is commonly called the "Defense Eagle." Stock cartouches are discussed more fully in the section on Stocks, Inspection Cartouche.

Heat Treatment Lot Numbers
Heat treatment lot numbers were applied to critical parts manufactured from a specific lot of steel that had undergone heat treat-

The M1 Garand

ment. The heat treatment lot number was marked on three parts, receiver, barrel and bolt, to permit tracing in case a problem developed. They were usually a letter/number combination and did not necessarily follow a numerical or alphabetical sequence. The combination designated the steel's manufacturer and the particular heat treatment lot.

CONVENTIONS

1. Following the editorial practice of North Cape Publications, Inc., major changes to parts are classified as "Types." For instance, "two kinds of lower barrel bands were developed and used. The first is designated as Type 1 and the second as Type 2," etc. This system is used for the convenience of collectors only and was never used by the U.S. Ordnance Department.

Within "types," minor changes were often made to parts during the manufacturing period. These are referred to as "variations." For instance, the stock ferrule was made in two types and within the Type 2, are found three variations which concern the size of the hole in the forward lip. In many cases, such variations are helpful in determing the manufacturer of an otherwise unmarked part, i.e., International Harvester and Harrington & Richardson made stock ferrules with the large, 0.190-inch-diameter hole only.

2. Much of the specific documentation pinpointing changes in manufacture, shape, markings, etc. for the M1 Garand rifle no longer exists. Facility closures, downsizing and destruction of outdated documents have obscured many of the changes to the M1 Garand in the eight decades and more since the rifle was conceived.

At the National Armories, changes were implemented by work orders approved by the Ordnance Department. Following a practice established at the Springfield National Armory at the end of the 18th century, manufactured parts were used up first when safety was not a concern, before a new part was introduced. Parts were drawn from bins or racks and assembled into finished rifles. These were replenished at intervals, not when they were empty. Thus an "old" part could lie in the bottom of the bin or at the back

11

of a rack for several weeks or even months before being drawn out and used.

With very few exceptions, changes to the M1 Garand cannot be pinpointed to a specific serial number. Thus most parts' changes are described as taking place at "circa serial number XXX." Circa means "about." All "circa serial number XXX" ranges have been established according to observations made by the authors, and by many other researchers. Those are credited when known.

When the parts' changes were introduced over a period of time, the serial number range may be given as: XXX-XXXX to XXXXX. It should be understood that the first two sets of serial number are the range in which the change was introduced and the third set of numbers, the "to XXXXX," encompass the range in which the original part and the new part were being used together until the original parts were used up.

3. In this text, all markings on a rifle part or other issue item are shown in quotation marks, i.e.,

"U.S./SEMIAUTO. RIFLE/CAL. .30 M1/
SPRINGFIELD ARMORY"

The quotation marks were not part of the marking unless so noted. The slash (/) indicates a line break.

4. When measurements are given from a point to a hole or other opening, that measurement is understood to be to the center of the hole or opening, unless otherwise noted.

5. All reference directions are given from the shooter's standpoint while looking toward the muzzle with the rifle shouldered. Thus right side refers to the side with the bolt handle, etc.

6. Line drawings of parts are often used in preference to photographs for clarity or to emphasize certain aspects. Occasionally, a drawing or part of a drawing is exaggerated to emphasize a point. Where exaggeration is used it is noted in the text and/or caption.

The M1 Garand

7. The M1 Garand was manufactured according to the English measurement system. All dimensions are given in decimal inches. Non-North American readers can easily convert measurements from decimal inches to millimeters by multiplying by 25.4. Example: 2.3 inches x 25.4 = 58.4 millimeters or 5.84 centimeters.

8. Four discrete numbers may be found on many Garand parts, as described above, that will help identify the period of manufacture and use. These numbers are mentioned in the text describing each part.

First is the serial number, found only on the receiver.

Second is the drawing number of the part which referred to the actual Ordnance Department-approved drawing and which established its manufacturing specifications. As the part was modified, the drawing number was amended by adding a suffix number or letter to the part, i.e., "D28287" is the drawing number of the bolt body. At circa Springfield Armory serial number 550,000 a change was made to it which was indicated by the addition of "-12" to the drawing number. Some parts also received the initials of the manufacturer: "SA" for Springfield Armory or "W" for Winchester Repeating Arms. Thus the full marking for the bolt body manufactured by Springfield Armory between serial #s 550,000 and 3,200,000 is "D28287-12SA." Not all parts were marked with a drawing number.

The third number is the steel lot or the heat treatment lot number. This is usually found only on bolt bodies as well as some barrels and receivers.

The fourth numerical identifier is the date of manufacture in the form of numbers for Month/Year. This is only found on barrels.

9. Information may be repeated several times in the text at different points so the reader does not have to page back and forth.

The M1 Garand

Officer Candidates at Ft. Benning, GA, in 1941 examining the M1 Garand (gas trap) rifles they have just been issued.

A soldier from Battery C, 27th Field Artillery, 6th Infantry Division, fires an early "gas trap" M1 Garand in training during 1941.

The M1 Garand

4th Armored Division infantrymen fire at German troops as they advance to the relief of Bastogne on December 27, 1944. U.S. Army photo.

Infantrymen of the 3rd Bn., 148th Rgt., 37th Division, cross a stream on New Georgia in pursuit of retreating Japanese. U.S. Army photo.

The M1 Garand

New Zealand and U.S. Army troops compare each other's battle rifles. The New Zealander holds an M1 Garand rifle while the American examines his Enfield No. 1 Mk. III* rifle, probably manufactured at the Small Arms Factory, Lithgow, NSW, Australia.

The M1 Garand

An American soldier fires his M1 Garand at enemy troops along the highway north of Balate Pass on the Philippine island of Luzon. U.S. Army photo.

Troops of the 397th Infantry advance through a cleared German obstacle in the High Vosges in November 1944. U.S. Army Signal Corps Photo.

The M1 Garand

U.S. 100th Division troops crossing a mountain ridge in the German Winter Line in December 1944.

U.S. 25th Division infantrymen on a ridgeline fire their M1 Garands at North Korean troops in July 1950. U.S. Army photo.

The M1 Garand

M1 Garand, Winchester manufacture, October 1943. North Cape Publications collection.

M1 Garand National Match, Type 3C, 1964. North Cape Publications collection.

M1C Garand Sniper Rifle, Springfield Armory, 1951. Woody Travis collection.

The M1 Garand

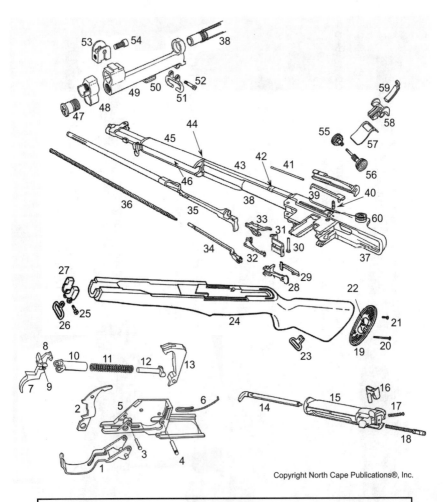

Copyright North Cape Publications®, Inc.

M1 Garand	
Exploded View	
1. Trigger Guard	7. Trigger
2. Safety	8. Sear
3. Trigger Pin	9. Sear Pin
4. Trigger Guard Pin	10. Hammer Spring Housing
5. Trigger Housing	11. Hammer Spring
6. Ejector Clip Spring	12. Hammer Spring Plunger

The M1 Garand

M1 Garand	
Exploded View	

13. Hammer
14. Firing Pin
15. Bolt Body
16. Extractor
17. Extractor Plunger & Spring
18. Ejector & Spring
19. Butt Plate
20. Butt Swivel Screw
21. Butt Plate Screw
22. Butt Plate Cap
23. Butt Swivel
24. Stock
25. Stock Ferrule Swivel Screw
26. Stock Ferrule Swivel
27. Stock Ferrule
28. Follower
29. Cartridge Slide
30. Follower Arm Pin
31. Bullet Guide
32. Follower Arm
33. Operating Rod Catch
34. Follower Rod Assembly
35. Operating Rod
36. Operating Spring
37. Receiver
38. Barrel
39. Clip Latch
40. Clip Latch Spring

41. Clip Latch Pin
42. Rear Handguard Band
43. Rear Handguard
44. Lower Band
45. Front Handguard
46. Front Handguard Liner
47. Gas Cylinder Lock Screw
48. Gas Cylinder Lock
49. Gas Cylinder
50. Bayonet Mount
51. Stacking Swivel
52. Stacking Swivel Screw
53. Front Sight
54. Front Sight Screw
55. Windage Knob
56. Rear Sight Elevation Pinion and Knob
57. Front Sight Cover
58. Front Sight Base
59. Aperture
60. Front Sight Housing

This cover photo used on previous editions shows some of the equipment issued to the World War II combat infantryman. Clockwise from left, the M1 steel helmet, .30-06 ammunition in carton, en-bloc clip, and bandolier, M1 Garand manual, M1 bayonet, and M1923 dismounted belt. The M1 Garand at the top was made in January 1944 and is from the collection of Craig Reisch. The M1C Sniper rifle below is from the collection of John Capalbo.

A Marine instructor demonstrates the proper kneeling position with an M1 Garand at Camp Pendelton, California in the summer of 1943. USMC Photo.

The M1 Garand

CHAPTER 2
THE M1 GARAND, PART-BY-PART

As in previous books in the "For Collectors Only" series, the authors feel that the best way to analyze a collectible firearm is on a part-by-part basis, relating any changes that occurred during the manufacturing process to the serial number range. This allows the collector to determine whether a change was "officially ordered" or spurious.

In the M1 Garand, this process is complicated by the lack of an official serial number list and complete production records. But production numbers by month have been worked out by Scott Duff, a well-known expert on M1 Garands (see Appendix A) and which he generously allowed us to use in this volume. His production numbers from inception in August 1937 to the wartime end in July 1945 are widely accepted and have been verified by comparison to numerous original M1 Garands. By adding these monthly numbers and making adjustments for duplicate serial numbers between Springfield and Winchester and numbers that were allotted but not used on actual receivers, a fair approximation of serial number ranges by month can be derived. Comparing this monthly listing of serial numbers with a wide range of M1 Garands considered to retain their original barrels, the authors have determined that barrel dates can lag the receiver's manufacture—as determined by the serial number—by up to three months in the latter stages of production. This may reflect the ordnance department's desire to have as large an inventory of parts available against emergencies and shortages of materials.

The authors wish to emphasize that the word *circa* means "at, in or approximately" and is used exactly in that context. A serial number "range" is given for each change to a part. In some cases that range encompassed tens of thousands of finished rifles; in other instances, as few as hundreds. The collector should keep in mind that the nation was engaged in total war against the Axis powers and virtually nothing was allowed to go to waste. Nearly all parts were "used up" even as they were being superseded by a new or revised design.

23

The M1 Garand

RECEIVER

PHYSICAL CHARACTERISTICS

The receiver drawing number was D28291. It was 8.60 inches long by 1.675 inches wide at the widest point. The receiver was forged and machined to shape. See Figures 1 and 2.

The receiver had four "legs" which held the trigger housing, follower rod assembly, follower arm, follower assembly, bullet guide and operating rod catch assembly in place. It also had nine holes or slots: 1) barrel opening 1.10 inches in diameter, 2) rear sight pinion assembly hole 0.370 inch in diameter, 3) bolt assembly well 3.535

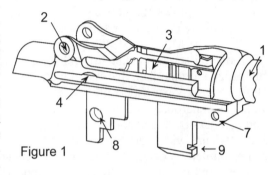

Figure 1

inches long by 1.10 inches wide, 4) operating rod groove 5.095 inches long by 0.275 inch wide, 5) clip latch assembly groove 2.15 inches long by 0.265 inch wide, 6) clip latch hole on the left rear leg, 7) hole 0.145 inch in diameter for the follower pin arm counterbored to 0.20 inch, 8) hole 0.30 inch

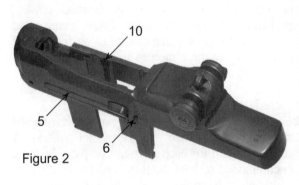

Figure 2

in diameter on the right rear left leg and 9) notch on front legs 0.125 inch high by 0.15 inch deep.

Between circa serial #s 81-79,100 to 92,600 the right and left clip guides in the magazine well just ahead of the follower showed

The M1 Garand

a beveled area at the top. Refer to Figure 2 (Arrow 10) and see Figure 3. This bevel was cut during the drilling as well as the later broaching process for the barrel. The drill or broach was accidentally allowed to penetrate far enough to bevel the top of the guides. This round cut or bevel (high rib in Figure 3) on each side contributed to a condition known as the "7th round misfeed" that plagued Springfield engineers until the reason for it was discovered in the autumn of 1940. The drilling and later broaching process was altered to prevent the top of the clip guides from being beveled (low rib in Figure 3) and a square cut was seen once again. Most rifles between circa serial #s 81-92,600 had the problem corrected by welding metal to the top of the clip guides. When examining an M1 Garand in this serial number range which is purported to be "original and unaltered," examine the bevels at the top of the clip guides to make certain it is beveled.

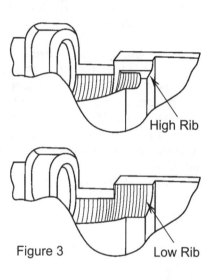

High Rib

Figure 3

Low Rib

At circa serial #1,787,000, cracks appeared in the rear legs of some Springfield M1 receivers at the point where the trigger assembly clamped shut. For a short period between circa serial #s 1,787,000-1,877,000, the receiver leg was annealed to reduce the brittleness, leaving a slight discoloration on the lower leg of some receivers. After circa serial #1,977,000, a slight increase in the radius of the fillet (0.0005 inch) solved the problem.

Springfield and Winchester M1 Garands may show the rear section "darker" in color than the front and sides, as the rear of some M1 receivers were dipped in molten lead to relieve stress and reduce the hardness to prevent cracking. If a bolt failed during firing, the annealed metal would bend and stop the bolt, rather than crack and allow the bolt to strike the shooter in the face. Subsequent receivers were manufactured to the proper hardness and show no discoloration.

Differentiating Between Manufacturers of M1 Garand Receivers
Springfield, Winchester and International Harvester machined the outside of their receivers so that sharp, crisp edges remained. Harrington & Richardson relieved all sharp edges for a rounder appearance.

Early Springfield receivers were cut square at the rear of the bolt lug travel slot until the gas trap series ended circa serial #85,000; after, the cut was round. Winchester used this same square cut for all receivers until circa serial #2,400,000 when it was changed to round. David H. McClain, who has kept detailed records on M1 Garand receivers, points out that the transition from square to round cut presently encompasses a range of 32,000 serial numbers. The Win-13 series, circa serial #s 1,600,000-1,640,000, made in 1945, also had the round cut.

NOTE 1: Winchester M1 Garands in the serial number range 1,600,000-1,640,000 are sometimes called the Win-13 series by collectors after the drawing revision number "WIN-13" stamped on the right receiver leg. Win-13 rifles were built out of serial number sequence and were manufactured between January 1945 and the end of Winchester production in June 1945. Note also that these numbers duplicated numbers assigned to Springfield.

NOTE 2: Some receivers were manufactured for International Harvester by Springfield Armory and Harrington & Richardson. They can be identified by the Springfield and Harrington & Richardson styles of receiver drawing numbers in Table 3. H&R receivers can further be identified by their smooth, rounded edges and their very late IHC serial numbers (circa serial #5,200,000). Only Springfield-made receivers, though, will show a heat lot number.

Receiver Material
Early receivers were made of War Department Steel No. 3115. To July 1942, War Department Steel No. 3120 was used. After, War

The M1 Garand

Department Steel No. 8260 Modified was used. The receiver was carburized (hardened) to a depth of 0.012-0.018 inch at 1,600 degrees F, then quenched in oil. It was then tempered at 480 degrees F to Rockwell D59 to D67 hardness.

Receiver Markings—All receivers were stamped with the following information on the rear section behind the rear sight: U.S. RIFLE/CAL. .30 M1/MANUFACTURER'S NAME/ SERIAL NUMBER. Until serial #80, the word "SEMIAUTO" was included before the word "RIFLE"; from serial #81 on it was dropped from the marking. Table 2 presents all known variations of the M1 Garand receiver markings. At circa serial #s 1,100,000-1,200,000, the size of the serial numbers on the Springfield receivers was reduced from 0.11 inch to 0.90 inch high. At circa serial #2,350,000, the line "Trade Mark" in the Winchester receiver marking was reduced in size to 0.20 inch long so that the entire line fit approximately between the "C" and "S" in the line above. International Harvester receiver markings underwent several changes in spacing as shown.

Heat Lot Numbers—Each batch of steel used for receivers was heat treated and the number of that batch stamped on Springfield and some Harrington and Richardson receivers but not Winchester. Only International Harvester receivers made by Springfield will show the heat lot number.

Drawing Numbers—Receivers were stamped with the drawing number D28291 on the right front leg. The dash and numbers following the drawing number represent drawing "revisions." Above the drawing number was also stamped the heat treat lot for the batch of steel from which that receiver was made.

The M1 Garand receiver underwent numerous changes that required revisions to the drawing number. These are listed in Table 3. When inspecting an M1 Garand, it is advisable to compare the serial number range and the drawing number. Demilled receivers that have been rewelded with front and rear halves from different receivers will often show drawing numbers on the front of the receiver that are not consistent with the serial number shown on the rear of the receiver.

Other Receiver Markings—When M1 Garands were rebuilt, and in many cases, refinished in the late 1950s and 1960s, the initials

The M1 Garand

Table 2		
M1 Garand Receiver Markings		
	U.S. SEMIAUTO. RIFLE CAL. .30 M1 SPRINGFIELD ARMORY **80**	
U.S. RIFLE CAL. .30 M1 SPRINGFIELD ARMORY **81**	U.S. RIFLE CAL. .30 M1 WINCHESTER TRADE MARK **1001201**	U.S. RIFLE CAL. .30 M1 *WINCHESTER* TRADE MARK **2300000**
U.S. RIFLE CAL. .30M1 INTERNATIONAL HARVESTER **4452398**	U.S. RIFLE CAL. .30 M1 INTERNATIONAL HARVESTER **4441723**	U.S. RIFLE CAL. .30 M1 INTERNATIONAL HARVESTER **4643723** (*)
	U.S. RIFLE CAL. .30 M1 H.&R. ARMS CO. **5762190**	* Also used in the circa serial # 5,207,000 range

of the armory doing the work, and the date performed were engraved with an electric pencil on the right leg. The example shown at the right indicates "Springfield Armory, May 1963."

SA
5-63

The M1 Garand

Table 3 M1 Garand Receiver Drawing Numbers	
Drawing Number	**Serial Number Range**
Springfield	
D28291	1-16,000
D28291-1	16,001 - 35,000
D28291-2	35,001 - 65,000
D28291-3SA	65,001 - 247,000
D28291-9SA	247,001 - 280,000
D28291-12SA	280,001 - 350,000
D28291-13SA	350,001 - 400,000
D28291-14SA	400,001 - 490,000
D28291-17	490,001 - 1,500,000
D28291-27	1,500,001 - 1,765,200
D28291-29	1,765,201 -1,900,000
D28291-30	1,900,001 - 2,300,000
D28291-32	2,300,001 - 2,850,000
D28291-34	2,850,001 - 3,000,000
D28291-35	3,000,001 - 3,888,000
D652891-42	4,206,000
D652891-43	5,458,000
F 652891	6,099,905
Winchester	
D28291-2	165,500 - 2,320,100
D28291WIN-13	1,600,000 - 1,640,000
International Harvester	**Date Range**
D652891-42	1953
D652891-43	1953
IHCD6528921-A	1953
D6528291-C	1953
D6528291-D	1953
D6528291-G	1953
D6528291-H	1953

The M1 Garand

Table 3, cont. M1 Garand Receiver Drawing Numbers	
Drawing Number	**Date Range**
D6528291-I	1953
D6528291-J	1953,1954
D6528291-L	1954
D6528291-M	1953, 1954
D6528291-N	1953, 1954
IHC F 6528291	1953
Harrington & Richardson	
6528291	1953, 1954
D-6528291	1953
D652891-J	1954
D652891-L	1954
D652891-P	1954
D652891-Q	1954
652891-X	1954
D652891-Y	1954
D652891-AA	1954
D652891-E	1955

Determining If a Receiver Has Been Demilitarized

Demilitarizing is a term applied to military equipment removed from service. In the late 1940s and throughout the 1950s when the M1 Garand was still in service and not available to the shooting public, damaged or obsolete M1 Garands were "demilled" by sheering, crushing or cutting with a saw blade or torch across the center. They were then sold for scrap. Enterprising persons bought some of these scrapped receivers, welded them back together and mated them with used surplus, relined-G.I. or new-made barrels and other parts. Many were identified at the time as having been demilitarized but in the intervening years that distinction has often been lost.

There are two ways to identify receivers remanufactured from de-milled receivers. The easiest and most accurate way is to have the receiver X-rayed at an industrial X-ray facility (check your yellow pages). Unfortunately, it is also relatively expensive, ranging in cost from $60 to $200.

The second method is not as certain but is far less expensive. Remove the receiver/barrel assembly from the stock and examine carefully by eye. An 8X or 10X loupe or a strong magnifying glass will be helpful. Receivers which were demilitarized may show evidence of the cut made across the receiver and through the rails, but a sharp eye and a strong magnifying glass will be needed. By aligning two halves of a receiver in a jig, an experienced gunsmith could reweld them into a working receiver. Welding always hardens metal on either side of the weld. This shows up clearly in an X-ray, but may also be visible to the naked eye. In bare metal, look for brighter stripes of metal outlining the weld. If a Parkerized finish was applied over the weld, look for darker stripes with uneven edges outlining the weld. Look also for tiny flaws—bubbles or pits—left when the molten metal flowed together. Use your loupe or magnifying glass to search for any change in the texture of the metal or finish. Examine the original machine-made marks in the receiver slots and rails. Where the welded area was recut you may see a different pattern of cutter or polish marks and the texture of the metal may be different. Check also the tops of rails to see if they show any sudden narrowing or changes in color or polish. Any such defect as described above should lead you to see the entire weld.

CLIP LATCH ASSEMBLY

The function of the clip latch (Figure 4) was to hold the 8-round en-bloc clip in place against the upward pressure of the clip ejector spring and follower arm. The clip latch assembly consisted of the clip latch, the clip latch retainer spring and the clip latch pin. By holding the bolt to the rear and depressing the clip latch, the clip and any unfired cartridges can be ejected manually.

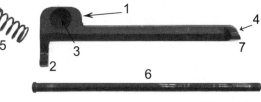

Figure 4

The M1 Garand

Clip Latch

The clip latch (drawing number C46011) was 2.85 inches long and the integral thumb piece (1) at the rear was 0.5 inch high by 0.6 inch long. The tail on the latch clip (2) depended 0.4 inch below the thumb piece and was 0.1 inch wide. The inside surface of the thumb piece had a blind hole 0.285 inch in diameter and 0.195 inch deep drilled to secure the clip latch spring in place (3). A hole 0.20 inch in diameter was drilled the length of the clip latch for the clip latch pin (4). Many clip latches appear to have been rough cast and ground to tolerance. Early Springfield and early Winchester clip latches only were blued; the rest were Parkerized.

There were two types of clip latches: the **Type 1** front end (7) was round and the **Type 2** was square, see Table 4. International Harvester clip latches may show a "letter" which is thought to indicate an inspection acceptance. Those marked "A" are often passed off as Winchester clip latches but only they manufactured the rounded front end Type 1 clip latches.

Table 4 Clip Latch Identification Guide		
Type	**Description**	**Serial # Range**
Springfield		
1A	Rounded front end at top, marked "-O" or "O" (used primarily with gas trap rifles)	81-50,000
1B	Rounded front end at top, unmarked	50,001-2,110,000 to 2,720,000
2	Squared front end. During war production, mix of round, semi-round and square front ends. Cuts are rough and appear ground by hand.	2,110,000-2,272,000 to end of production
Winchester		
1B	Rounded front end, unmarked, punch mark	100,001-1,280,000 and 1,600,000-1,640,000

The M1 Garand

	Table 4, cont.	
	Clip Latch Identification Guide	
Type	**Description**	**Serial # Range**
1C	Rounded front end, many but not all marked "CM"	1,280,000 Mixed use to EOP
1D	Rounded front end, many but not all marked "A" on outside	1,333,683 Mixed use to EOP
International Harvester		
Springfield 2	Squared front end, inspector's initials ("A" or "C") beside spring retaining hole on inside	4,400,000-4,660,000 and 5,000,501-5,278,245
Harrington & Richardson		
Springfield 2	Squared front end, unmarked	4,660,001-4,800,000 and 5,488,247-5,793,847

Clip Latch Spring
The clip latch spring (refer to Figure 4, part 5) functioned to press the clip latch outward when a loaded clip was inserted into the breech, thus retaining the clip. When the clip latch was depressed with the thumb, the clip was unlatched and the pressure exerted by the follower arm and follower assembly ejected the clip.

All clip latch springs were five coils of steel wire 0.03 inch in diameter. The outside diameter of the spring was 0.26 inch. The bottom coil was slightly oversized to retain its seat in the clip latch. No changes were made to the clip latch spring during its production by any manufacturer. The clip latch springs were originally left in the white. A clip latch spring that has been Parkerized usually indicates refinishing.

Clip Latch Pin
The clip latch pin (refer to Figure 4, part 6) held the clip latch in place in its cutout on the left, upper side of the receiver. The clip latch pin used by all four manufacturers was 3.280 inches long overall. It had a head 0.155 inch in diameter and 0.065 inch high.

The M1 Garand

The opposite end was rounded slightly. The body of the pin was 0.119 inch in diameter. No changes were made to the clip latch pin throughout production.

Originally, clip latch pins were blued but late post-World War II clip latch pins appear to have been finished with a smooth polish which provided a less grainy Parkerizing.

REAR SIGHT ASSEMBLY

The rear sight for the M1 Garand was fully adjustable for windage and elevation to 1,200 yards. The rear sight assembly used a rack and pinion gear mechanism to adjust for elevation. See Figure 5. The battle range or battle sight for the M1 Garand was set at 300 yards. On early versions of the M1 Garand sight, this setting was marked on the elevation knob with a small ▲. When the rear sight elevation pinion was improved in 1947, it was omitted for lack of room. All parts were Parkerized. The rear sight mechanism underwent a series of changes between 1942 and 1944 (but not used until 1947) which resulted in three distinct types of rear sights.

NOTE: In actual fact, this sight assembly (T105E1) was approved and adopted in late 1944 but was not installed until the post-World War II years (see Duff, Bibliography, Appendix K). As an aside, when the wartime sight was set at the "battle-sight setting," and M1 ball or armor-piercing ammunition was used, the rifle would shoot to point of aim at 300 yards, but strike 5.5 inches high at 100 yards and 14 inches low at 400 yards. This battle-sight setting was considered effective against man-sized targets to 400 yards.

Rear Sight Elevation Pinion—The rear sight elevation pinion allowed the shooter to adjust the elevation, It was essentially a round knob attached to a shaft machined with pinion-type teeth which meshed with the gear on the bottom of the aperture. Turning the rear sight elevation pinion by means of the knob raised or lowered the aperture. Springfield manufactured three variations of the rear sight elevation pinion and Winchester, two. See Figure 6.

Rear Sight Elevation Pinion: Type 1—The overall length of the rear sight elevation pinion (shaft and inner knob) was 1.830 inches. The inner knob was 0.670 inch in diameter and 0.169 inch thick.

The M1 Garand

The diameter of the geared shaft was 0.270 inch and each of the twelve teeth was 0.395 inch long and 0.027 inch wide at the top. The center was drilled and tapped to accept a screw that secured the outer cover to the inner knob. The screw was 0.320 inch long. It had a flat head with angled shoulders 0.231 inch in diameter and a 6-40NF thread. Reproduction screws have been noted with very shallow screwdriver slots. Refer to A in Figure 6 (which is shown without the outer cover).

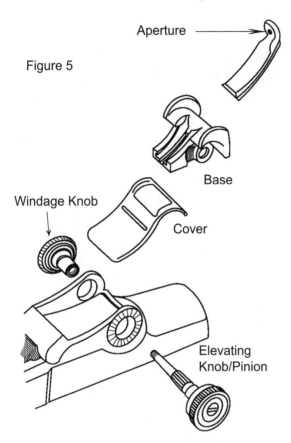

Aperture

Figure 5

Base

Windage Knob

Cover

Elevating Knob/Pinion

The outer cover was 0.80 inch in diameter across the knurled edge and 0.735 inch in diameter across the inner edge. This edge was stamped with the numbers "2," "4," "6," "8," "10," and "12" in sans serif letters 0.09 inch high to indicate range in hundreds of yards. Short lines perpendicular to the edge subdivided the range into one-hundred-yard increments.

Two variations of the outer cover for the Type 1 Rear Sight Elevation Pinion were manufactured. The **1st Variation** used (circa serial #s 46,000-47,000) had the drawing number "B-8872"

The M1 Garand

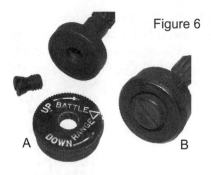

Figure 6

stamped on the inside, and also, checkered edges. The **2nd Variation** did not show the drawing number. Both variations of the outer cover for the Type 1 Rear Sight Elevation Pinion were marked on the outside, "Up →," "Down →," "Battle ▲ Range." Slight variations in type style and size of markings will be noticed throughout production. It had a hole 0.190 inch in diameter in the center, surrounded by a 0.0240-inch chamfer. A slotted screw held the cover to the pinion knob. This elevation pinion was secured with the "flush nut."

Rear Sight Elevation Pinion: Type 2—If the soldier needed to change the elevation setting of his rear sight, he had to unlock the flush nut with the combination tool which was an inefficient and unhandy practice, especially in battle. To eliminate this problem, a locking bar was added to the end of the rear sight elevation pinion shaft which could be manipulated by hand without a tool. The locking bar also eliminated the problem of the rear sight aperture changing elevation when the rifle was fired.

The original rear sight elevation pinion remained in use but the windage knob nut was exchanged for a locking bar which screwed onto the 6-40NF threaded end of the pinion shaft. The locking bar was tightened against the windage knob to hold the rear sight elevation pinion assembly in place under recoil. See the descriptions of the Locking Bar below under Rear Sight Lock Nut.

Rear Sight Elevation Pinion: Type 3—The early **1st Variation** locking bar had a tendency to loosen and fall off during use. To overcome this problem, the rear sight elevation pinion was lengthened by 0.125 inch and the thread size on the end of the pinion shaft was changed to 8-36NF. A **2nd Variation** locking bar was designed with an 8-36NF thread. It screwed onto the pinion shaft which was counterbored. The end of the shaft was staked into the counterbore to hold the locking bar in place. This rear sight

The M1 Garand

elevation pinion can be readily identified by its longer shaft, longer teeth (0.575 inch), 8-36NF thread and counterbored end. Late Springfield locking bars have squared ends; Winchester locking bars have rounded ends.

The earliest versions of the **Type 3** Rear Sight Elevation Pinion, used to circa serial #3,000,000, had the pinion shaft end radiused to match the locking bar. After circa serial #3,000,000, the end was finished square.

NOTE: Four variations of the rear sight elevation pinion shaft have been observed with a groove cut around its circumference at the left end of the shaft. What appeared to be the earliest **1st Variation** had a groove 0.085 inch wide and 0.035 inch deep separating the teeth from the shaft. This size groove was associated with the first type rear sight elevation pinion with the short (0.395 inch) teeth. The **2nd Variation** with the long teeth (0.575 inch) ending in a rounded "V" had a narrow, shallow groove (0.035 inch wide x 0.001 inch deep) cut 0.095 inch ahead of the teeth. A **3rd Variation** with the long teeth ending in a narrow "V" also had the wide, deep groove cut through the teeth 0.275 inch from the end of the pinion shaft. The groove, which was 0.085 inch wide and 0.04 inch deep, left the tip ends of the teeth visible. A **4th Variation** either had no groove or else had a barely discernible groove in the same location as the second variation. It was not possible to quantify these variations with regard to serial number but the 3rd and 4th Variations appear to have been in use at about the same time.

Rear Sight Elevation Pinion: Type 4 (Elevating Knob and Screw)—The Type 4 Rear Sight Elevation Pinion is more properly called the Elevating Knob (drawing number C46002). It was manufactured as an integral assembly without a cover. Elevation settings are marked directly on the side of the knob, "2," "4," "6," "8," "10," and "12" indicating the range in hundreds of yards. Lines scribed between the numbers indicated the next step in range in 100-yard increments. The rear sight assembly not only showed the shooter the range at which his rear sight was set, but positive "click" stops served both to help hold the sight setting under recoil and to allow the shooter to set the sights by touch and

The M1 Garand

hearing at night, or when he could not risk looking down. By turning the sight down to its lower setting, then both listening to and feeling for the clicks as the knob was turned, he could, by counting clicks, reset the elevation. Each click raised the point of impact of M2 Ball .30-06 issue ammunition by one minute of angle (one inch at one hundred yards). There were sixty clicks to one full revolution of the elevation knob. In addition to the manufacturers' markings listed in Table 6, Type 4 Elevating knobs may also be marked "SSH," "NHC," "LUX," and "W" within a triangle, according to Dave Clark and Scott Duff. Refer to Figure 6B.

Table 5 summarizes the types of elevation pinions and Table 6 the elevation knobs.

Windage Knob—The windage knob (right side) adjusted the movement of the rear sight aperture from side to side. It had 32 threads to the inch and was Parkerized. One turn of the windage knob moved the aperture 1/32 or 0.03235 inch to the side, see Figure 7. Like the elevation knob, the windage knob provided a tactile and audible signal to the to the shooter. One "click" moved the aperture 0.0078125 inch which was not quite one minute of angle (0.96 inch at 100 yards).

Figure 7

The knob and collar were assembled as one piece. Overall height was 0.750 inch. The outside diameters of the collars were 0.370 and 0.270 inch respectively below the threads. The end of the collar was threaded. All windage knobs were Parkerized.

Three types of windage knobs were used. The **Type 1** or earliest production windage knobs to circa serial #195,000 can be identified by their checkered edges. The windage knob flush nut and spring could be removed. See Figure 8.

Type 2 windage knobs manufactured between circa serial #s 195,000-198,000 to 3,800,000 were knurled. The windage knob flush nut or lock bar and spring could be removed. See Figure 9.

The M1 Garand

	Table 5	
	M1 Garand Rear Sight Elevation Pinions	
	Identification Guide	
Type	**Description**	**Serial # Range**
1	Short with 6-40NF thread, with flush nut. Early examples (to circa #s 46,000-47,000) were marked inside with the part number	SA 1-540,000 WRA 100,001-1,280,000
2	Short, same as Type 1 but with locking bar substituted for flush nut, 6-40NF thread	SA 540,000-1,000,000 (mixed use)
3	Long with 8-36NF thread, with locking bar	SA 800,000-3,800,000 WRA 1,280,000-end of production
4	Postwar with 8-36NF thread, no locking bar	SA, IHC, HRA- All post-WW II production

	Table 6	
	M1 Garand Elevation Knob Cover Identification Guide	
Type	**Description**	**Serial Number Range**
Springfield		
1A	Part number inside, checkered rim (closed arrowheads)	1-46,000 to 47,000
1B	No part number, checkered rim (closed arrowheads)	46,000-47,000 to 850,000
1C	Knurled rim (closed arrowheads)	850,000-3,890,000
2	Postwar, integral part of pinion. May be marked "SA" in late 1950s+	4,206,000-6,099,905, plus all M1 Garands that underwent refurbishment.
Winchester		
1A	Checkered rim, early closed arrowheads. Later open arrowheads more common	100,001-1,240,000
1C	Knurled rim (open arrowheads)	1,240,001-1,380,586 and 2,305,850-2,533,060 and 1,600,000-1,640,000

The M1 Garand

Table 6 , cont. M1 Garand Elevation Knob Cover Identification Guide		
Type	**Description**	**Serial Number Range**
International Harvester		
2	Postwar, integral part of pinion, may be marked "IHC DRC"	4,400,000-4,660,000 & 5,000,501-5,278,245
Harrington & Richardson		
2	Postwar, integral part of pinion, may be marked "HRA-W" or "HRA"	4,660,001-4,800,000 & 5,488,247-5,793,847

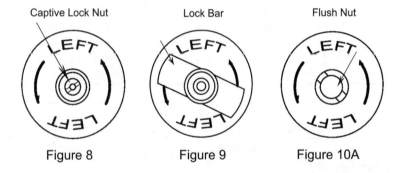

Captive Lock Nut   Lock Bar   Flush Nut

Figure 8   Figure 9   Figure 10A

Type 3 windage knobs used on all Springfield M1s manufactured after circa serial #4,200,000 plus all International Harvester and Harrington & Richardson M1s used a windage knob with a captive lock nut that could not be removed. No spring was installed. These were also used on M1 Garands rebuilt during "Clean and Repair" programs during and after 1945. See Figure 10A.

All windage knobs were marked "←**Left**" "←**Left**." Springfield windage knobs were characterized by closed arrowheads while Winchester-manufactured windage knobs had open arrowheads. Those marked "WH" were manufactured by Weatherhead, a subcontractor in the early to mid-1950s. They have "open" arrowheads. "SA"-marked windage knobs were manufactured in the 1950s at Springfield. They were used on some National Match M1 rifles, M1 Garands that were refurbished in the 1960s, and the M14 rifle.

The M1 Garand

Rear Sight Lock Nut—The rear sight lock nut was fitted inside the windage knob shaft and was threaded to receive the threaded end of the rear sight elevation pinion. Early rear sight lock nuts used with the Type 1 and Type 2 rear sight elevation pinion had a 6-40NF thread. Later Type 2C lock nuts had an 8-36NF thread. The locking bar lock nut was rectangular in shape and 0.750 inch long by 0.260 inch wide. It had two binding ridges on the underside 0.134 inch thick which bore against the windage knob, and a counterbored hole in the center (0.180 inch in diameter), the interior of which was threaded to accept the 6-40NF (**Type 2A**) or 8-36 NF (**Types 2B** and **2C**) threaded pinion shaft. The rear sight lock nut served to hold both the elevation and windage settings against recoil or other disturbances. See Table 7 and refer to Figures 8-10A and see Figure 10B.

2A   2B   2C

The **Type 1** locking nut was a flush nut that required the spanner on the end of the Type 1 combination tool to manipulate. It was used only on the Type 1 rear sight elevation pinion.

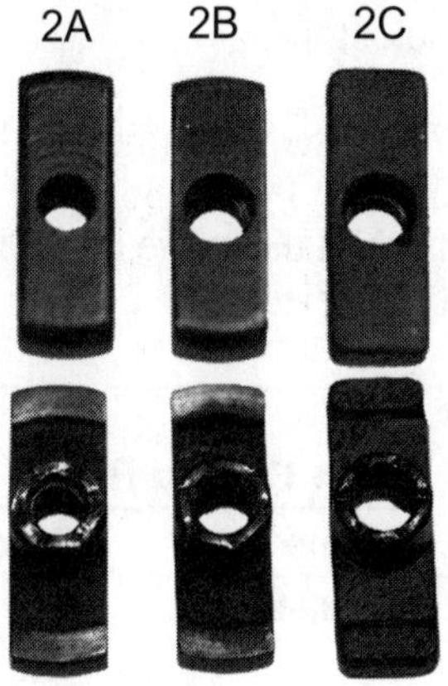

The **Type 2** series of lock nuts as manufactured by Springfield Armory were improved by the use of an external locking bar that could be tightened or loosened with the fingers. A three-coil spring exerted pressure between the windage knob and the locking bar Figure 10B to hold the elevation and windage settings. They were used with the Type 2

Figure 10B

and 3 rear sight elevation pinions. Three variations of the Type 2 locking bar were used, see Figure 10B. The ends were beveled slightly where the flat outer surface ended at top and bottom.

The **Type 2A** locking bar was distinguished from the Type 2B locking bar by its 6-40NF thread and was used with the short Type 2 rear sight elevation pinion. It had shallow rounded ends that did not match the curve of the windage knob. The binding ridges on the interior ends followed the same curve. It was in use from circa serial #s 530,001 to 1,000,000.

41

The M1 Garand

The **Type 2B** locking bar had an 8-36NF thread and was used with the long Type 3 rear sight elevation pinion. It had shallow rounded ends that did not match the curve of the windage knob. The binding ridges on the interior ends followed the same curve, refer to Figure 10B. The Type 2B was in use from circa serial #s 1,000,001 to 2,500,000.

The **Type 2C** locking bar also had an 8-36NF thread and a long pinion but its ends were squared off as were the binding ridges on the interior, refer to Figure 10B. It was in use from circa serial #s 2,500,001 to 3,890,000 on the long Type 3 rear sight elevation pinion.

As noted above, the Type 4 rear sight elevation pinion did not require a separate locking bar as the setting was maintained by click stops.

Winchester-manufactured locking bars were similar to the Springfield Armory Type 2 locking bars but had more fully curved ends that matched the curve of the windage knob. The locking bar ends were not beveled.

Table 7 M1 Garand Rear Sight Lock Nut Identification Guide		
Type	**Description**	**Serial # Range**
Springfield		
1	Flush Nut (short pinion, 6-40NF thread)	1-530,000 See Figure 8
2A	Locking Bar (short pinion, 6-40NF thread) with rounded ends and rounded binding ridges	530,001-1,000,000 See Figures 9 and 10B. See Table Note (1) below
2B	Locking Bar (long pinion, 8-36NF thread) with rounded ends and rounded binding ridges	1,000,001-2,500,000 See Figures 9 and 10B. See Table Note (1) below
2C	Locking Bar (long pinion, 8-36NF thread) with squared ends and squared binding ridges	2,500,001-3,890,000 See Figures 9 and 10B. See Table Note (1) below

The M1 Garand

Type	Description	Serial # Range
	**Table 7, cont.**	

Table 7, cont.
M1 Garand Rear Sight Lock Nut Identification Guide

Type	Description	Serial # Range
3	Windage Knob Nut, no locking bar, 8-36NF thread with square ends and square binding ridge	4,206,000-6,099,905 See Figure 10A
Winchester		
1	Flush Nut (short pinion, 6-40NF thread). Also, locking bar rounded ends match curve of knob, no beveled top surface	100,001-165,000 and 1,200,000-1,310,000
2B	Locking Bar (long pinion, 8-36NF thread), locking bar rounded ends match curve of knob	1,310,000-1,380,586 and 2,305,850-2,533,060 and 1,600,000-1,640,000
International Harvester		
3	Windage Knob Nut See Table Note (2) below	4,400,000-4,660,000 and 5,000,501-5,278,245
Harrington & Richardson		
3	Windage Knob Nut See Table Note (2) below	4,660,001-4,800,000 and 5,488,247-5,793,847

(1) Type 2B and Type 2C locking bars were used together during transition until the supply of Type 2As was exhausted.
(2) Neither International Harvester nor Harrington & Richardson ever installed locking bar sights on rifles of their manufacture.

Windage Knob Spring—The windage knob spring exerted pressure between the windage knob and the windage knob lock nut to hold the rear sight elevation pinion knob at a specified range setting. This was accomplished by pushing it against its outer cover, where it was held in place by teeth on the side of the cover and the outside of the rear sight elevation pinion knob.

The M1 Garand

The spring used with the Type 1 and Type 2 windage knob was made of wire 0.032 inch in diameter. The spring had 3.5 coils and an outside diameter of 0.25 inch. The spring was ground flat on both ends and was left in the white.

No coil spring was used with the Type 3 windage knob. Its spring tension derived from a flat, circular spring that was installed on the Type 3 elevation pinion knob. This windage knob cannot be disassembled.

Rear Sight Base
The rear sight base provided a housing for the rear sight assembly. The rear sight base was 0.185 inch high by 1.235 inches long. The rear portion with the protective ears was 1.350 inches wide and the forward portion containing the track for the aperture was 0.590 inch wide. See Figure 11.

The **Type 1** rear sight base was made in two variations: **Type 1A** was marked with the drawing number, C46001, stamped on the flat underside and machined with a rounded area behind the hole for the elevation/windage knot shaft (A). The hole which accepted the rear sight elevation pinion and windage knob was bored 0.280 inch in diameter and was threaded to accept the windage knob assembly. A concentric ring was machined around the circumference of this hole. It was used to circa serial #25,000. **Type 1B** was identical to Type 1A but was not marked with the drawing number on the underside. It was in use to circa serial #75,000.

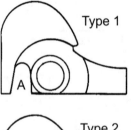

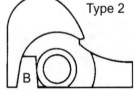

Figure 11

Type 2 lacked the drawing number, the concentric ring around the hole for the rear sight elevation pinion/windage knob assembly was eliminated and the area behind the hole for the elevation/windage knob assembly was "squared" off (B). This variation was used to the end of production.

The M1 Garand

Winchester manufactured the **Type 1B** and it had the typical rough finish. Some Winchester rear sight bases starting at circa serial #165,000 may also show the marking "CM." Winchester also manufactured rear sight bases for the M14 rifle in the 1960s which were identical to those used on the M1 Garand. They were marked "OF" on the base with a code letter/number. They are occasionally found on M1 Garands which were arsenal rebuilt after 1959.

International Harvester rear sight bases were either unmarked or were stamped "A" or "C." Harrington & Richardson rear sight bases manufactured for the M1 Garand were unmarked. Those built for the M14 were marked "H&R" followed by a code number/letter combination. Again, these may turn up on M1 Garands which were arsenal rebuilt after 1959.

Aperture
Five major types of the M1 Garand rear sight aperture were used. Four were manufactured by Springfield and a fifth by Winchester. Harrington & Richardson and International Harvester used the Type 3 aperture developed by Springfield. Refer to Figure 5.

The Springfield aperture was milled from solid steel. It was 1.380 inches long by 0.445 inch wide. The length of the curved ramp was 1.30 inches; the outside diameter of the aperture disk was 0.363 inch by 0.120 inch thick (measured horizontally across the peep hole). The diameter of the sighting hole in the aperture was 0.065 inch and 0.120 inch thick where the aperture disk joined the ramp. The aperture was Parkerized and its rear face (facing the eye) was cross hatched to eliminate glare by a punch tool that produced a pattern of dots. The aperture had seventeen teeth centered in a line along the bottom curve to mesh with the teeth on the rear sight elevation pinion. The teeth were 0.125 inch wide.

The **Type 1** aperture used to circa serial #20,000 on rifles manufactured with the gas trap system did not have tracks cut into the bottom surface on either side of the teeth. It was stamped with the drawing number, B8868-1, on the upper curved surface.

The M1 Garand

The **Type 2** aperture was used from circa serial #s 20,000 to 28,000. It did not have the tracks on the bottom on either side of the teeth and the drawing number was omitted.

The **Type 3** aperture used from circa serial #28,000 through the end of production had tracks cut into the bottom surface on either side of the teeth. The earliest Type 3 apertures had very shallow, narrow tracks 0.065 inch wide that quickly were enlarged to 0.085 inch wide by 0.02 inch deep. Early manufactured Type 3, **1st Variation** apertures had rounded-ramp shoulders below the aperture disk; the later **2nd Variation** apertures had squared shoulders. The edges of the aperture disk were smoothly finished.

The **Type 4** aperture was developed for fine target shooting at long ranges and therefore, the diameter of the sight hole or "peep" was smaller on the side facing the shooter. The first apertures designed for the National Match Rifles were part #s 7268110 and 7268109 with peep holes of 0.0520 and 0.0595 inch respectively and were mounted on standard bases. They were installed on National Match Rifles as early as the Type 2.

The **Type 5** aperture was also developed for fine target shooting at long ranges and therefore, the diameter of the sight hole or "peep" was smaller on the side facing the shooter. The aperture was covered by a hood to shut out extraneous light. The hood was 0.45 inch long by 0.47 inch in diameter. The exterior of the hood was knurled with the knurl lines running fore and aft in relation to the eye. The curved ramp was marked on the top, "NM" for National Match in sans serif letters 0.08 inch high. Two sizes of sight hole or "peep" were manufactured, 0.0520 and 0.0595 inch in diameter. Also refer to Appendix C. The Type 5 "hooded" aperture was installed on Types 3C and 3D National Match Rifles starting in 1962.

The Winchester **Type 1** aperture was "stamped" from sheet steel rather than milled from a steel ring as were the Springfield apertures. Winchester apertures were distinguished by a thicker base that sloped into the curved upper surface of the ramp (refer to arrow in Figure 5) and no tracks on either side of the gear. They were 1.380 inches long by 0.450 inch wide. The length of the curved ramp was 1.30 inches. The outside diameter of the aperture disk was 0.370 inch by 0.145 inch thick (measured horizontally across the "peep" hole) and 0.230 inch where the aperture disk joined the ramp. The diameter of the peep hole in the aperture was 0.065 inch on the side facing the eye and opened up to 0.130 inch on the side facing the target. The length of the curved ramp was 1.30 inches. The aperture was Parkerized. The face of the Winchester-manufactured aperture showed a crosshatch pattern which was formed by thin lines crossing each other at a 60-degree angle. The Winchester-manufactured aperture was never marked with a drawing number but often was marked with a punch mark on the bottom surface.

The Winchester **Type 2** aperture was identical to the Type 1 except for tracks cut on either side of the teeth, or gear, on the bottom of the aperture. These were used only in the Win-13 series, serial #s 1,600,000-1,640,000. This same Type 2 aperture was used on M14 rear sights manufactured by Winchester in the 1960s (personal communication from Scott Duff to Simeon Stoddard).

Rear Sight Cover

The rear sight cover (drawing number B8872) was a rectangle of sheet metal curved to match the slope of the rear sight base, refer to Figure 5. It was 1.850 inches long when the base was horizontal, 1.09 inches wide and 0.50 inch high. The cutout for the rear sight base was 0.895 inch wide by 0.565 inch long. Early Springfield and Winchester rear sight covers were blued but the majority were Parkerized. Early Springfield Type 2 rear sight covers have a dark, frosty appearance and a punch mark. Winchester's rear sight covers are light gray-green. Two types and four variations of Springfield-manufactured, and two types of Winchester rear sight covers have been identified.

The M1 Garand

Table 8 M1 Garand Rear Sight Cover Identification Guide		
Type	**Description**	**Serial # Range**
Springfield		
1A	Smooth, no reinforcing indentations along top and sides. Was marked "B-8872"	81-10,000
1B	Smooth, no reinforcing indentations along top and sides. Was marked "B 8872"	10,000-20,000
1C	Smooth, no reinforcing indentations along top and sides. Was marked "8872"	20,000-50,000
1D	Smooth, no reinforcing indentations along top and sides. Not marked.	50,000-95,000
2	No drawing number marked, 0.140-inch-wide reinforcing indentations stamped on right and left edges. Third indentation perpendicular to edges 0.070 inch wide and 0.660 inch long, spaced 0.20 inch below opening for aperture.	95,000 to end of production
Winchester		
1	Similar to Type 1D Springfield, without markings, thinner spring steel 0.40 inch thick. Early, blued, most light gray-green Parkerizing	100,001-105,000 to 116,000
2	Similar to Type 2 Springfield, thinner spring steel 0.40 inch thick, light gray-green Parkerizing	105,001-116,000 to end of production
International Harvester—similar to Type 2 Springfield during entire production		
Harrington & Richardson—similar to Type 2 Springfield during entire production, but indentations struck deeper		

The M1 Garand

BOLT

The M1 Garand bolt was composed of seven parts: bolt body, firing pin, extractor, extractor spring, extractor plunger, ejector and ejector spring. From the start of production until circa Springfield serial #536,000, bolts were made of WD Steel No. 3312. After, all bolts by all manufacturers were made of WD Steel No. 8620 Modified. The difference was the addition of molybdenum as an alloying agent. See Figure 12.

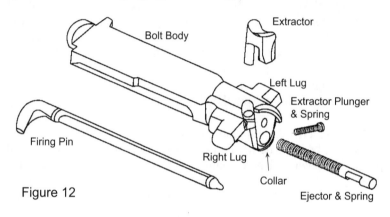

Figure 12

Bolt Body

The M1 Garand bolt body was 3.80 inches long. The following measurements will suffice to identify an original M1 bolt body. The front end was cylindrical (0.705 inch in diameter) and formed a "collar" which was cut away in two arcs, at the seven o'clock position for the extractor and at the five o'clock position. The top segment of the collar was 0.635 inch long by 0.120 inch thick by 0.115 inch high. The bottom segment was 0.485 inch long by 0.120 inch thick by 0.115 inch high.

The face of the bolt body was pierced by two holes. The center firing pin hole was 0.075 inch in diameter and the bottom ejector hole was 0.140 inch in diameter. The top front of the bolt body was round in cross section for 0.970 inch to the center of the curve. Thereafter, the bolt body was flattened with a concave surface for 2.90 inches where it resumed a rounded cross section again. The rear rounded section of the bolt was 1.80 inches wide

49

The M1 Garand

and 0.720 inch in diameter. The rear section contained one firing pin hole that extended into a slot for the firing pin tail to the five o'clock position. The rear firing pin hole was centered and 0.210 inch in diameter and the slot was 0.165 inch wide and 0.25 inch long. The rear of the bolt body also included a triangular cut 0.30 inch wide, 0.190 inch from center to periphery and 0.230 inch deep at the deepest point.

The original M1 Garand bolt had only one hole in the underside of the bolt body. It was for the extractor post and was 0.170 inch in diameter and centered 0.40 inch from the front of the bolt to the right of the midline. Springfield added a second hole in the center of the bolt underside at circa serial #55,000 and Winchester at circa serial #110,000. The second hole was 0.075 inch in diameter and was centered 1.530 inches from the front of the bolt.

NOTE: Several theories have been advanced for the center hole in the bolt body. One holds that it was for lubricating the internal parts. However, all field manuals caution against lubricating the firing pin and other internal parts. Another theory suggests that it was a drain hole for water. A third theory suggests that it was a gas escape hole in case of a blown primer or ruptured case as with the Model 1903 bolt.

At the front, two lugs were machined to fit into guide slots or rails in the receiver. The right lug was stepped: the outer step was 0.365 inch long by 1.85 inches wide by 0.30 inch high. The inside step was 0.575 inch long by 0.210 inch wide by 0.315 inch high at the front by 0.290 inch high at the back. The left lug was 0.465 inch long by 0.165 inch high at the front by 0.295 inch high at the rear.

The M1 Garand bolt body was marked with the drawing number and any revision number immediately followed by the manufacturers' initials, i.e., SA=Springfield, WRA=Winchester, IHC=International Harvester, HRA=Harrington & Richardson Arms, and the steel heat treatment lot number (except Winchester). The bolt body drawing number was D28287. Drawing revision numbers used through World War II were 1, 2, 5, 12, 17, 18, and 19. Drawing number 6528287SA was used on post-World

The M1 Garand

War II M1 Garands. A typical arrangement of drawing number, revision number, manufacturer and heat treat lot number is shown in Figure 13.

D28287-12SA
W98◇

Bolts made according to the first drawing number revision and marked "-1" have sans serif lettering 0.09 inch high with the "-1" beneath the drawing number. The "-2" and all subsequent drawing number revision markings are 0.075 inch high and are marked in one line.

Postwar M1 Garand bolts made by International Harvester were marked in three ways: 1) D-6528287IHC, 2) D6528287 IHC and 3) 6528287 IHC. On IHC bolt bodies, the letter "U" is often centered below the drawing number. It is a heat lot mark and does not indicate manufacture by Underwood. Also, a combination of letters and numbers may be found on the top left side of the bolt indicating the heat treatment lot.

Postwar M1 Garand bolt bodies made by Harrington & Richardson were also marked in three ways: 1) D6528287 HRA, 2) 6528287 HRA and 3) 6528287 H.R.A./U.W. The first two variations will usually, but not always, show the letter "U" beneath the drawing number. The third variation drawing number was followed by two letters and the heat treat lot number on the left side of the bolt in line with the "U.W." Underwood may have manufactured these bolts for Harrington & Richardson.

Directly above the drawing number will be found a Rockwell Hardness quality-control-test punch mark or indentation on the bolt. All M1 Garand bolts were Parkerized except very early Springfield and Winchester bolts. Table 9 identifies all known M1 Garand bolts.

EXTRACTOR
Only one type of extractor, drawing number C46003, was used on all M1 Garands manufactured by Springfield, Winchester, International Harvester and Harrington & Richardson. See Figure 14.

The M1 Garand

Table 9		
M1 Garand Bolt Identification Guide		
Marking	**Serial # Range**	**Comment**
Springfield		
D28287	1-15,000	No hole in underside of bolt body, no "SA"
D28287-1	15,000-55,000	No hole in underside of bolt body, no "SA"
D28287-2SA	55,000-550,000	Hole in underside of bolt body, "SA" stamped after revision number
D28287-5SA	Very small quantity produced, if any. Insufficient data to fix serial number range	Hole in underside of bolt body, "SA" stamped after revision number
D28287-12SA	550,000-3,200,000	Hole in underside of bolt body "SA" stamped after revision number
D28287-14SA	Limited use, if any	Revision adopted 6/20/42, no bolts with this designation yet seen
D28287-17SA	3,200,000-3,250,000	Hole in underside of bolt body, "SA" stamped after revision number
D28287-18SA	3,250,000-3,300,000	Hole in underside of bolt body, "SA" stamped after revision number
D28287-19SA	3,300,000-3,890,000	Hole in underside of bolt body, "SA" stamped after revision number

	Table 9 , cont. M1 Garand Bolt Identification Guide	
Marking	**Serial # Range**	**Comment**
6528287SA	4,200,001-4,3999,999; 5,000,000-5,000,500; 5,278,246-5,488,246; 5,793,848-6,099,905	All post-World War II bolts—hole in under-side of bolt body, "SA" stamped after revision number
Winchester		
D28287-1WRA	All serial numbers	Early production to circa serial #110,000, extractor post hole only. After, second hole added in bottom of bolt
International Harvester		
D-6528287IHC D6528287 IHC 6528287 IHC	4,400,000-4,660,000; 5,000,501-5,278,245	Hole in bottom. "U" mark is a heat lot identification and does not indicate Underwood manufac-ture. "IHC" stamped after revision number
Harrington & Richardson		
D6528287 HRA 6528287 HRA 6528287 H.R.A./ U.W.	4,660,001-4,800,000; 5,548,827-5,793,847	Hole in bottom. It appears that all bolts used in HRA M1 Ga-rands may have been made by Underwood. They were usually marked "UW" below the drawing number. The third-style bolt showing "H.R.A./ U.W." also shows a heat lot number

The M1 Garand

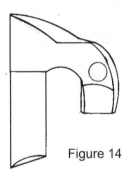

Figure 14

Springfield-manufactured extractors were blued or Parkerized during World War II; all were Parkerized after. Winchester-manufactured extractors were blued throughout production. The most reliable indicator to Winchester-manufactured extractors is a punch mark. International Harvester and Harrington & Richardson extractors and those for the M14 rifle are identical to Springfield-manufactured extractors.

Extractor Spring and Plunger Assembly

The extractor spring assembly was composed of two parts, the spring and the extractor plunger, both assigned drawing number B8886. The overall length of the assembly was 0.525 inch. No changes were made to the extractor spring assembly throughout production. The plungers were blued or

Figure 15

Parkerized—blued were the earliest. See Figure 15.

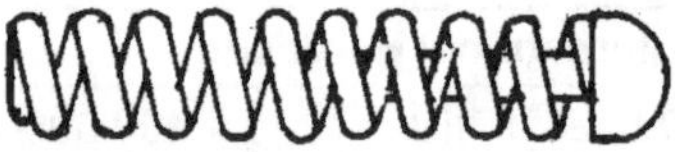

The extractor plunger was 0.310 inch long by 0.156 inch in diameter. It had a tail 0.240 inch long by 0.060 inch in diameter over which the extractor spring fitted. The plunger head was rounded and fit into a round cut in the rear of the extractor.

The extractor spring was 0.122 inch in diameter and had ten coils. It was made of 0.026-inch-diameter wire. The extractor spring was ground flat on the ends and was left in the white. Late examples may be Parkerized.

There were no discernible differences between the extractor spring assemblies manufactured by Springfield, Winchester, International Harvester or Harrington & Richardson, or those manufactured for the M14 rifle.

EJECTOR

The ejector was a short, rod-shaped piece of spring-loaded steel that pushed the cartridge rim away from the extractor's grip and

The M1 Garand

allowed the cartridge to be thrown clear of the receiver. See Figure 16.

Figure 16

The ejector was 0.580 inch long by 0.150 inch in diameter. A semicircular relief channel 0.260 inch long and 0.06 inch deep was cut to pass the ejector mounting post. The ejector had a protrusion on the rear 0.05 inch in diameter and 0.05 inch long over which the ejector spring was fitted. Springfield ejectors were blued, later Parkerized. Winchester ejectors were blued throughout production.

Two Springfield ejector drawing numbers were used. From the start of production to circa serial #2,500,000, drawing number B8873 was used. After, drawing number B8616 was used. There were no apparent physical differences in ejectors made according to either drawing number and the change may have involved a change in steel or heat treatment.

NOTE: The Springfield Armory annual report for Fiscal Year 1944 shows a total of 81,333 ejectors (drawing number B8873) plus 837,460 (drawing number B8616) manufactured. Thereafter, ejector drawing number B8616 was listed in all succeeding annual reports.

Ejector Spring

The ejector spring (drawing number B8884) was attached to the rear of the ejector. Refer to Figure 16. The spring was 0.120 inch in diameter and made of steel wire 0.015 inch in diameter. The spring had twenty-eight coils and was nominally 1.210 inches long. Replacement ejector springs were manufactured at Springfield under drawing number A196462 in Fiscal Year 1946, and under drawing number A7313885 from Fiscal Year 1947 on. The ejector spring was ground flat on the ends. The majority of ejector springs were left in the white; others show a deep gray-black color. M14 rifle ejector assemblies look the same as those for the M1 Garand but the M14 ejector spring was 1.625 inches in length, 0.415 inch longer.

The M1 Garand

FIRING PIN

Two types of firing pins were used. The **Type 1** firing pin was round in cross section from the start of production to circa serial #s 400,000-425,000. The **Type 2** firing pin was machined to a half-round configuration to provide more freedom of movement, to reduce friction and the possibility of binding. The firing pin drawing number was B8879. See Figure 17A.

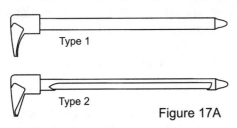

Figure 17A

The firing pin was "L" shaped and 3.770 inches long by 0.185 inch in diameter at the nose and 0.210 inch in diameter at the rear just before the short stroke of the "L." The modified firing pin after circa serial #s 400,000-425,000 was relieved one half its diameter beginning 0.250 inch from the tip of the nose for a distance of 2.95 inches. The short stroke of the "L" was 0.560 inch long and was ground flat on the sides and back to a thickness of 0.135 inch. The nose was 0.170 inch long, see Figure 17B.

Early Springfield firing pins were blued; wartime firing pins were blued or Parkerized and those produced in the 1960s had a chrome-plated nose.

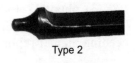

Type 2

Winchester switched from the round to the half-round firing pin at circa serial #1,200,000. Winchester firing pins can only be distinguished—if at all—by their slightly rougher machining and the Rockwell Hardness punch mark. Winchester firing pins were either unfinished or blued.

Type 1

Figure 17B

International Harvester and Harrington & Richardson firing pins were similar to the Springfield Type 2 firing pins and were Parkerized.

56

The M1 Garand

BARRELS

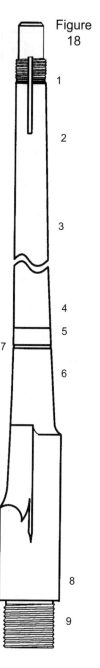

Figure 18

Two types of M1 Garand barrels were man-ufactured. The first was the "Gas Trap" barrel in which gas from the fired cartridge used to power the action was trapped between the end of the barrel and the gas cylinder plug. The order to change from the Gas Trap system to the Gas Port system, in which gas from the fired car-tridge was bled directly from the barrel to im-pinge upon the gas piston, was issued on October 26, 1939. The changeover occurred in production at circa serial #50,000 in July 1940.

The M1 Garand barrel (see Figure 18) was made of War Department Steel No. 4150 Modified. Tensile strength was 130,000 lbs per square inch (Brinell hardness—269 to 311, equivalent to Rockwell C28 to C34). The gas trap barrel draw-ing number, D28286, was stamped on top of the barrel. The drawing number for the gas port bar-rel was D35448, and it was also stamped on top of the barrel until 1953 when it was moved to the right side under the operating rod handle.

BARREL DIMENSIONS

Gas Trap barrels were 22 inches long and had a single spline 0.650 inch long cut into the barrel ahead of the threads to the muzzle, see Figure 19. The barrel at the muzzle was 0.580 inch in diam-eter. Threads for both gas trap and gas port bar-rels were 10 per inch, 0.052 inch deep ± 0.003 inch (measured at 1/2-way-down thread) and set at an angle of 29 degrees.

The Gas Port barrel was 24 inches long, and had a step (1 in Figure 18) 0.595 inch in diameter cut 1.120 inches behind the muzzle leading to the gas port area which was 0.970 inch long. Its drawing number was D6535448 until circa mid- to late-1953 when the "D" prefix was dropped. Sometime

The M1 Garand

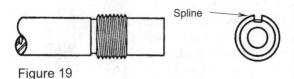

Spline

Figure 19

thereafter, the prefix was changed to "F" and continued in use to the end of production.

Three splines 1.335 to 1.340 inches long when measured from the start of the step were cut through the gas port area. The barrel was 0.515 inch in diameter at the muzzle. See Figure 20.

The gas port was located on the bottom surface of the barrel. It was 0.0805 inch in diameter and was centered 1.5 inches from the muzzle.

Beyond the gas port area, the barrel stepped down to 0.585 inch (2) in diameter, refer to Figure 18.

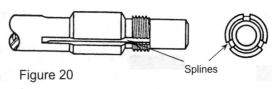

Figure 20

Splines

After 3.375 inches, a second step was machined into the barrel which increased the diameter to 0.625 inch (3). This step was 7.85 inches long and was 0.695 inch in diameter (4) just ahead of a collar machined around the barrel to which the rear handguard clamped. The collar (5) was 0.730 inch in diameter and 0.45 inch long. A slot 0.4 inch long by 0.1 inch wide was cut on the bottom of the collar for the pin that held the barrel band in place.

NOTE: Springfield barrels had a circular cut or ring behind the collar (7 in Figure 18), deepened along the bottom for the lower band pin. Winchester barrels did not have this ring. Instead, a simple groove was cut in the bottom of the barrel for the lower band pin.

The third step ended in a compound step or flare. Measured along the top, it was 0.760 inch in diameter (6) and flared to 0.890 inch (7) after 4.610 inches. Measured along the bottom of the barrel it was 4.865 inches long. Barrel diameter at the rear, just ahead of the threaded shank, was 1.10 inches in diameter (8). The threaded shank was 0.970 inch in diameter and was 0.70 inch long (9).

The M1 Garand

Between the third and final step, the barrel was relieved on top 0.110 inch to reduce weight. The length of this relieved area was 2.725 inches.

Two slots were cut to accept the rear handguard band. The slot on the right side was 0.880 inch long and 0.065 inch wide at the end of the relieved area. The second slot on the left was cut 1.50 inches long and 0.065 inch wide. It was centered 0.45 inch above the bottom surface of the barrel and began 1.4 inches from the rear of the barrel, not including the shank.

NOTE: The above diameters will vary somewhat due to different machining processes. They are important as some M1 Garand barrels have been "modified" by certain unscrupulous persons who reduced the diameter in certain areas to eliminate import markings or change manufacturer's markings. Springfield-manufactured barrels have been identified with the Springfield markings ground off the right side and spurious Winchester markings restamped on top. To ascertain if a particular barrel has been so "modified," the M1 Garand barrel diameter exactly 3.5 inches behind the muzzle is 0.60 inch; at 4 inches ahead of the breech, the barrel diameter is 1.10 inches side to side and 0.985 inch top to bottom. Also look for the "index" or "witness" line or mark on the bottom of Winchester barrels only. The Marlin Firearms Company manufactured a small number of M1 Garand barrels during World War II. They appear to have been used as postwar barrel replacements and have been observed in Korean War-era Garands in the circa serial #4,200,000 range.

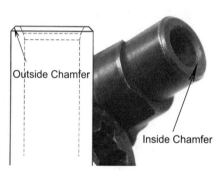

Figure 21

The M1 Garand barrel was crowned so that the very end was left flat, rather than rounded like the Springfield Model 1903. The inside and outside appear to have been chamfered, leaving the end flat. The chamfers are slightly rough in appearance. See Figure 21.

The M1 Garand

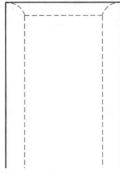

Figure 22

Barrels relined by commercial firms (see **Note**) have a different crown—high on the outside and rounding deeper into the muzzle. The machining was usually smooth and the crown was cut after the liner was brazed in place. Compare Figure 22 to Figure 21.

NOTE: During the 1950s, M1 Garand rifles were not available on the commercial market and only a few were being made available through the Director, Civilian Marksmanship Program. Several commercial companies purchased scrapped M1 parts at Government auction. M1 barrels were reamed out with a slight taper and relined using Model 1903A3 Remington barrels turned down to fit inside the Garand barrel. The majority of the Model 1903A3 barrels used had 2-groove rifling. They were installed primarily on receivers that had been rewelded. Modern reproduction barrel splines are usually ground rather than cut as were the originals. Check for lack of sharp edges and rough and uneven cuts through the threads for the gas cylinder lock.

BARREL MARKINGS

Gas trap barrels were marked with the drawing number "D28286-heat number" lot on top of the barrel in the relieved area under the rear handguard and were manufactured only at Springfield. The right side showed the proof "P," visible in the operating rod slot, but no month and year of manufacture. All Springfield barrel markings were applied with a roll die.

Gas port barrels were marked with the drawing number, "D35448-Revision Number-Heat Lot Number." The heat lot was an alphanumeric identifier but occasionally contained iconic symbols such as a diamond. They were also proofed ("P") on top, then after circa serial #254,000, on the right side, visible in the operating rod slot. Barrels manufactured in 1946 were marked on top; those in 1950s-60s were marked again on the right side.

The M1 Garand

Various inspector markings—letters and symbols—followed the heat lot number. Other inspector numbers or letters may be noted on the second and third step. Letters commonly observed are "M," "S," and "V."

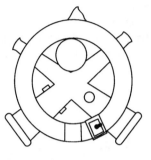

Figure 23

All World War II-era to September/ October 1953 original M1 Garand barrels show the Ordnance Department Crossed Cannon symbol (0.130 inch in diameter muzzle to breech) to the left of the drawing number, Figure 23. The Defense Acceptance stamp (see Figure 25C below) was substituted after September/ October 1953.

Rockwell Hardness punch marks are usually found on the top rear of the barrel, just ahead of the shank, on the left side of the barrel where it begins to taper ahead of the chamber or the right side just behind the last step. Not all barrels will show hardness punch marks.

The right side of the Springfield barrel under the operating rod was marked "S-A" for Springfield Armory before the month and year of manufacture. Other inspection marks will occasionally be noted in this area.

The marking "S-A" followed by the date on the right side of the barrel was stamped upside down to circa serial #840,000; after, right side up. Barrels dated as early as 9/42 have been observed with the marking in both directions, indicating this was the month the change was made.

After 1952, circa serial #4,210,000, the marking "S-A" on Springfield barrels was changed to "SA," followed by the drawing number, month and year. The heat lot number was also marked on the right side of the barrel under the operating rod. All International Harvester and Harrington & Richardson barrels were marked the same way.

The M1 Garand

Winchester barrels were stamped with the drawing number D35448W.R.A. 3.675 inches ahead of the receiver face. The barrel and marking stamp were held in a special fixture shown on Winchester fixture drawings identified by S. Stoddard (see Bibliography, Appendix K). From circa serial #s 100,001-165,650, it was on the top right side of the barrel behind the last step and was visible when the operating rod was back. After, it was placed on the top left side. The Winchester proof (see Figure 24) was also marked on the right side but covered by the handguard. The Ordnance Department acceptance stamp was often, but not always, stamped behind the Winchester proof. World War II Winchester barrels were not marked with the drawing revision number, steel heat lot or month and year of manufacture.

Figure 24

International Harvester M1 Garand barrels were manufactured by the Line Material Company of Birmingham, Alabama. They are marked on the right side with the manufacturer's initials, "LMR," the drawing number, "D6535448," the date (month and year) and the heat lot number, usually a mix of letters and numbers. LMR barrel markings are often prefixed by the letter "P" or "PP."

NOTE: LMR barrels have also been observed on some very late Springfield M1 Garands that appear to be all original. The barrels do not appear to be replacements.

Harrington & Richardson manufactured their own barrels. They are marked on the right side with the barrel drawing number, "D6528287," the initials "HRA" and the heat lot which is usually an alphabetical character. HRA M1 Garands in the circa serial # 5,600,000-5,700,000 range have been observed with barrels marked by the Line Material Company (LMR).

NOTE: Winchester manufactured M1 Garand barrels under government contract during 1966-67. These barrels were marked "*Winchester*" in italics—followed by the part number—and show the month and year of manufacture. They were used only as replacement barrels.

The M1 Garand

The majority of M1 Garand barrels on original rifles will show a barrel date close to the month the receiver was manufactured as determined by the serial number. Barrel dates during World War II may lag the month the receiver was manufactured by as much as three months. Barrels dated "46" through "49" were manufactured for use during the massive postwar "Clean and Repair" refurbishment program at Springfield Armory. No new rifles were manufactured during this period. See Figures 25A, B and C for the style and placement of markings on M1 Garand barrels.

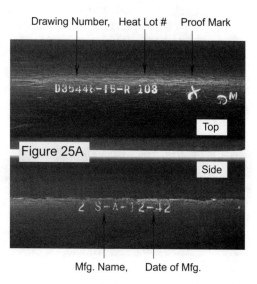

Drawing Number, Heat Lot # Proof Mark

Top

Figure 25A

Side

Mfg. Name,   Date of Mfg.

NOTE: Barrels made during the World War II years, 1942 to 1945, will usually show a prefix to the "SA" marking of "1," "2," or "3." Prewar and postwar barrels do not show this prefix. One theory has been suggested that M1 Garand barrels were allowed to be rejected and repaired no more than three times before they were scrapped. The number may identify the number of rejections and repairs. It should be noted the exact meaning on these numbers is unknown and that the suggestion made above is just a theory.

Starting at circa serial #s 4,320,000-4,350,000, the Defense Eagle Acceptance stamp was substituted for the Crossed Cannon cartouche, and marked on the right side of the barrel, after the heat lot number. The cartouche was 0.130 inch square. See Figure 25B for a drawing of the cartouche and Figure 25C for its location with other markings on a late-manufactured M1 Garand barrel.

The M1 Garand

Figure 25B

BARREL FINISH

All barrels made by any manufacturer or subcontractor were Parkerized—phosphate finish applied to the steel. Springfield barrels were originally gray-black in color. Exposure to oil and grease, especially cosmoline, often turned the Parkerizing to a deep olive green. Between circa serial #2,400,000 and the end of World War II, the Springfield Parkerizing process was changed to a thin gray-green color by leaving out the black dye from the oil bath. In sunlight, the greenish cast is readily evident. See also Figure 74.

Proof mark, Mfg., Drawing number,   Heat lot,   Mfg. date, Acceptance stamp

Figure 25C

The Parkerizing applied by Winchester was a light, flat gray-green. Winchester did not polish metal parts to the same extent as Springfield, or later International Harvester and Harrington & Richardson. As a result, the Parkerized finish will appear thinner, rougher and lighter in color than pre-serial #2,400,000 Springfield-applied Parkerizing.

International Harvester and Harrington & Richardson had Parkerizing which was black in color with just a hint of dark green in sunlight.

Barrels made by Springfield, International Harvester (LMR) and Harrington & Richardson from circa serial #4,200,000 to the end of production were chrome-plated around the gas port, which left a smooth, shining finish in this area. Barrels dated before 1950 which show chrome-plating in this area have been refinished.

NOTE: When barrels had the Parkerizing finish applied to them at Springfield, International Harvester and Harrington & Richardson, they were capped at both the muzzle and breech end before immersion in the Parkerizing solution. The breech end of the barrel visible when the bolt is open should be bright. If not, it has been refinished. Winchester barrels seem to have been finished either way, i.e., capped before Parkerizing or not capped and so the breech end may show bright or Parkerized.

BARREL RIFLING

The M1 Garand barrel was rifled with four grooves 0.1767 inch wide and four lands 0.0589 inch wide, which made one turn in ten inches (1:10) to the right. Many early "commercially rebuilt" M1 Garand barrels were sleeved with 1903A3 barrels, most of which had only two grooves. These are usually seen on welded receivers and must not be considered original military issue.

In the late 1950s and early 1960s, and again in the late 1990s to the present, several companies have offered "new" four-groove M1 Garand barrels for sale. These were not manufactured for government contracts but were made to be fitted to rewelded receivers (1950s and 1960s) or as replacement barrels on newly manufactured receivers (1990s to present). Many were marked with the company's name or initials, but others were unmarked. Be aware that some of these may now show up with counterfeit Springfield or Winchester markings added "after purchase."

There are also fine, newly manufactured barrels available from commercial outlets today. Many of these barrels have been manufactured by reputable firms for use in match-grade M1 Garands, using original or newly manufactured parts. These barrels should not be confused either with commercially rebuilt barrels which were usually relined with two-groove Model 1903A3 inserts or with original M1 Garand barrels made by the four manufacturers or by government subcontractors such as LMR or Marlin.

The M1 Garand

NATIONAL MATCH BARRELS

National Match barrels were selected after careful straightening and gauging. The barrel muzzle was crowned and concentric with the bore (60-degree angle) to remove any burrs. The threaded portion of the barrel against which the gas cylinder lock was tightened was cut so that the gas cylinder lock nut would bottom somewhere between the 6 and 8 o'clock positions.

The letters "NM" (0.13 inch high) were engraved on the barrel midway between the front handguard and the front sight on the left side of barrels installed on Types 2 and 3 National Match rifles. The Type 2 National Match barrel may also show a small six-pointed star after the "M," i.e., "NM*" as these were the only National Match rifle barrels whose bores were inspected using the star gauge.

The letter "P" indicating proof-firing showed a prick punch mark in the loop of the "P" on all National Match barrels. See Appendix C for a more detailed discussion of the National Match M1 Garand barrel.

The M1 Garand

OPERATING ROD ASSEMBLY

The operating rod and its components absorbed the energy from the gas bled from the barrel and used it to operate the bolt assembly.

OPERATING ROD

The operating rod was tubular for two thirds of its length, with a bend to the right leading to a squared cross section which contained the socket for the bolt lug and the handle by which the rifle was charged or operated. The operating rod used on the Gas Trap M1 Garand to circa serial #300 was made of sheet steel rolled into a tube and welded along its length. The weld was then ground smooth but remained visible under close inspection. After circa serial #300, all operating rod tubes were made of tubular steel and there was no weld seam. Overall, the operating rod was 21.55 inches long. Drawing numbers and other details are shown in Table 10, below. Also see Figure 26A.

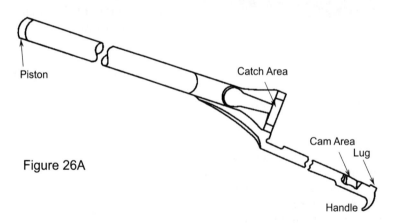

Piston

Catch Area

Cam Area

Lug

Figure 26A

Handle

Welded to the front of the tube was the piston against which propellant gases bled from the bore impinged. The piston was 0.525 inch in diameter and 0.180 inch thick. The end was polished flat with the forward edge feathered to 0.005 inch. The piston was assembled to the operating rod by the manufacturer and welded into place. It was not designed to be removed. If the piston needed repair, the entire operating rod was usually replaced. But if the

The M1 Garand

piston rod was found to be undersized, the piston could be plated and finish ground to the proper diameter as listed on Drawing D7790722.

Behind the piston was a tubular section 15.8 inches long which held the operating rod spring in place. It had an outside diameter of 0.505 inch and an inside diameter of 0.405 inch. The triangular area behind the tube contained the operating rod catches which engaged the notches on the operating rod catch assembly when the bolt was drawn to the rear. The rectangular projection at the right rear was the cocking handle. The lug which fitted into the track on the receiver was opposite the cocking handle, and the camming surface which engaged the right bolt lug was located within the hump of the operating rod, 1.4 inches ahead of the cocking handle.

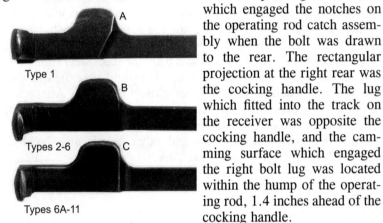

Type 1

Types 2-6

Types 6A-11

Figure 26B

Eleven types of operating rod were manufactured, but they are characterized by only four noticeable physical differences in the form of the "hump" which enclosed the cam area in which the bolt lug rode and the type of cut in the rectangular rod, see Figure 26B. The front of the hump in the **Type 1** operating rod was cut at a slant on the right (outer) side (A). In **Type 2** through **Type 6**, this same right, outer side area was cut vertically, but with a slight concave curve (B). In **Type 6A** through **Type 11** operating rods, this same right outer area was cut vertically but was straight from top to bottom, see Figure 26C.

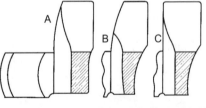

Type 1   Types 2-6 Types 6A-11

Figure 26C

The M1 Garand

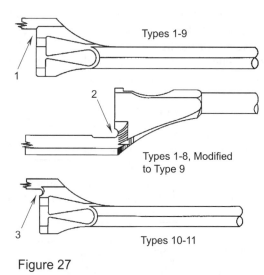

Types 1-9

Types 1-8, Modified to Type 9

Types 10-11

Figure 27

All operating rods (Types 1 through 6A) manufactured through World War II have a square cut where the handle attached to the tube, see Figure 27, arrow 1. This joint contained a sharp corner and it proved to be a point of stress which led to breakage during firing. After World War II, all rifles which were rebuilt had their operating rods modified (**Type 9**) with a radiused cut made at this junction to eliminate the sharp corner and strengthen the operating rod, refer to Figure 27, arrow 2.

All operating rods (**Types 10 and 11**) made after World War II were manufactured with the radiused cut (Figure 27, arrow 3). They were used both as replacements and for postwar production.

NOTE: It is not known exactly when **Types 7** and **8** operating rods were manufactured, but it is presumed that they were made from 1946 on. All that have been observed have the same radiused cut as the Type 9 operating rods.

The **Type 9** modified operating rod can include any Type 1 through 6A operating rod (and possibly Types 8 and 9) with drawing numbers between D35382-0 to D35382 9 SA which had a radiused cut made during refurbishing after World War II. The cut was 0.625 inch long, 0.0625 inch deep and had a radius of 0.0930 inch.

There were sixteen Springfield, three Winchester, and three International Harvester variations and a single Harrington &

The M1 Garand

Richardson variation of operating rods. Identification points are: 1) drawing number on the bottom behind the tubular section, above the engaging notches—except for the first variation; 2) shape of the milled cut on the bolt lug engagement recess; 3) relief cut in the arm joint area immediately behind the drawing number. 4) Most International Harvester operating rods are marked with a single letter which may have indicated an acceptance inspection.

Table 10 M1 Garand Operating Rod Identification Guide				
Type	Marking/ Position	Bolt Lug Housing Cut	Relief Cut (Radius Inches)	Circa Serial # Range
Springfield				
1A	D 28296 (top)	Slant	None	1-200
1B	D35382-0 (top)	Slant/curved top to bottom	None (1)	201-5,000
1C	D35382-0 (bottom)	Slant/curved top to bottom	None (1)	5,001-24,000
1D	None	Straight/ curved top to bottom	None (1)	24,001-34,000
2A	D35382-1SA or -1 SA (bottom)	Straight, con-cave curve	None (1)	34,001-38,000
2B	D35382-1-SA (bottom)	Straight, con-cave curve	None (1)	38,001-175,000
3	D35382 2 SA (bottom)	Straight, con-cave curve	None (1)	175,001-219,000
4	D35382 3 SA (bottom)	Straight, con-cave curve	None (1)	219,001-940,000
5	D35382 6 SA (bottom)	Straight, con-cave curve	None (1)	940,001-2,250,000
6	D35382 9 SA (bottom)	Straight, con-cave curve	None (1)	2,250,001-3,450,000
6A	D35382 9 SA (bottom)	Straight, straight top to bottom (flat side)	None (1)	3,450,001-3,850,000 (End of WW II Production)

The M1 Garand

	Table 10, cont. M1 Garand Operating Rod Identification Guide			
Type	Marking/ Position	Bolt Lug Housing Cut	Relief Cut (Radius Inches)	Circa Serial # Range
7	D35382 10 SA (bottom)	Straight, straight top to bottom (flat side)	5/16 (?)	Unknown
8	D35382 13 SA (bottom)	Straight, straight top to bottom, radiused cut	5/16 (?)	Unknown
9	D35382SA (bottom)	Straight, straight top to bottom, radiused cut	5/16	Used on armory-rebuilt rifles
10	653582SA (2) (bottom)	Straight, straight top to bottom, radiused cut	5/16	4,200,000 to end of production
11	7790722-RA or SA (bottom)	Straight, straight top to bottom, radiused cut	5/16	National Match Rifles from 1962
Winchester				
1A	D35382-W.R.A. (bottom)	Slant/curved top to bottom	None (1)	100,001-1,787,000
1B	D35382W.R.A. (bottom)	Slant/curved top to bottom	None (1)	1,787,001-2,574,000
6A	D35382W.R.A. (bottom)	Straight, straight top to bottom (flat side)	None (1)	1,600,000-1,640,000 (Win-13)
International Harvester				
10	D-6535382 IHC (bottom)	Straight, straight top to bottom, radiused cut	5/16	4,400,000-4,660,000

The M1 Garand

Table 10, cont. M1 Garand Operating Rod Identification Guide				
Type	Marking/ Position	Bolt Lug Housing Cut	Relief Cut (Radius Inches)	Circa Serial # Range
10	D6535382 IHC (bottom)	Straight, straight top to bottom, radiused cut	5/16	5,000,501- 5,150,000
10	6535382 IHC/a (bottom) (3)	Straight, straight top to bottom, radiused cut	5/16	5,100,000-End of Production
Harrington & Richardson				
10	6535382 HRA (bottom)	Straight, straight top to bottom, radiused cut	5/16	4,660,001- 4,800,000 5,488,247- 5,793,847

(1) May have been modified with a 3/16-inch radius during rebuilding from 1947 on.
(2) May also substitute the initials of the subcontractor for "SA."
(3) The drawing number 6535382 IHC was followed by a letter below on late production.

NOTE: Some Harrington & Richardson operating rods used on M1 Garand rifles toward the end of their contract (circa serial #5,790,000) have a rounded front cut at the top of the bolt lug engagement recess.

A special operating rod was designed for Type 3D National Match Rifles built after 1962 (see Appendix C). Outwardly, it was the same as the standard operating rod, but with a slight clockwise twist to fit it more snugly against the bolt ear. Its drawing number was 7790722-RA or SA. They are also marked "NM" on top of the cocking handle. The initials "RA" are for Remington Arms, "SA" for Springfield Armory. The same operating rod without the NM marking was also used in late sniper rifle rebuilds, and on very late standard M1 Garand rebuilds as well.

The M1 Garand

OPERATING ROD SPRING

The operating rod spring was fitted inside the operating rod's tubular portion for most of its length. The original operating rod spring (drawing number B46019), as used in the early "Gas Trap" and "Gas Port" rifle, and made by Springfield, was 0.385 inch in diameter and had 234 coils. See Figure 28. The wire was

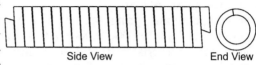

Side View   End View

Figure 28

"square" in cross section, left in the white and was used in conjunction with a "compensating spring," described below, to circa serial #160,000. Winchester used the "square" operating rod spring for the first few months of production to circa serial #102,000. It was 0.382 inch in diameter and had a slightly rounded upper surface. International Harvester and Harrington & Richardson never used the "square" operating spring.

This "square" spring is also sometimes referred to as "keystone-shaped" by other authorities.

After circa serial #160,000, Springfield Armory switched to a round spring (drawing number SA14675, later changed to B147658) manufactured by Wallace Barnes of Bristol, Connecticut, and eliminated the compensating spring, circa serial #s 70,000-79,000. Winchester switched to the round wire spring almost immediately after the start of production and eliminated the "compensating spring." See Figure 29.

Figure 29

The round operating rod spring was 0.380 inch in diameter and made of steel wire 0.055 inch in diameter. The spring had 188 coils and had to have been between 19 and 20.25 inches long to be serviceable. The end of the spring that fit over the shank of the follower rod was reduced in diameter to 0.320 inch so that it would remain firmly attached during firing. The round operating

The M1 Garand

rod spring was the same for all manufacturers and did not change during its production life. The spring was black in color although some appear blued and some were left in the white.

COMPENSATING SPRING

The compensating spring was used on Springfield M1 Garands to circa serial #s 70,000-79,000 and the earliest Winchester M1 Garands to circa serial #110,000, see Figure 30. Two types of compensating spring were used. **Type 1** was "square" in cross section and if made by Springfield, the wire was 0.040 inch in diameter and the spring was

0.315 inch in diameter. If made by Winchester, the wire was 0.038 inch in diameter and the

Figure 30

spring was 0.318 inch in diameter. Both had 55 coils. Winchester springs also had a slightly rounded upper surface in cross section. Both the Winchester and Springfield springs were left in the white. The **Type 2** compensating spring was also used with the Type 1 follower rod only (see below) to circa serial #s 70,000-79,000. It had 26 coils, was 4 inches long and approximately 0.30 inch in diameter, and left in the white.

FOLLOWER ROD ASSEMBLY

Five follower rods were developed. Identification details for the Follower Rod assembly are given in Table 11 and Figures 31-35. The first two types were round in cross section behind the shoulder that retained the spring. The **Type 1** was sized to fit both the compensating spring and the operating rod spring. The earliest Springfield and Winchester Type 1 follower rods were marked with the drawing number; later Type 1s were not. **Type 2** was used only with the operating spring and the shoulder was moved from the front of the rod to the rear. **Type 3** was made in four variations and used only by Winchester. **Type 4** was stamped from sheet metal, and a fork plate with stamped grasping grooves and a short slot was riveted to the rod. Because of problems with the follower rod slipping out of contact with the follower arm, on the **Type 5** the slot was cut more than double the previous length. The gripping grooves were also eliminated. All follower rods were Parkerized.

The M1 Garand

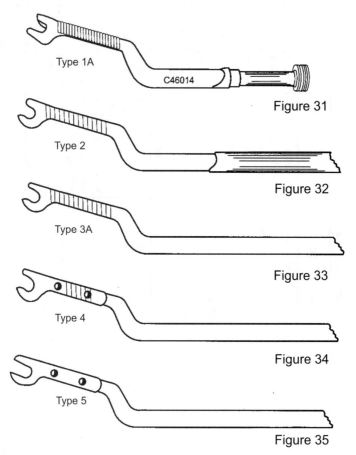

Type 1A

C46014

Figure 31

Type 2

Figure 32

Type 3A

Figure 33

Type 4

Figure 34

Type 5

Figure 35

OPERATING ROD CATCH ASSEMBLY

The operating rod catch was 2.575 inches long by 0.790 inch wide and 0.370 inch thick. Its drawing number was C46027 and it was composed of three parts: the op-

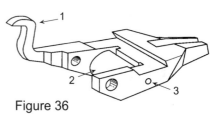

Figure 36

erating rod catch (1), the accelerator (2) and the accelerator rivet (3). See Figure 36. Type 1s were blued. Early Type 2s were left in the white to circa serial #740,000; after, they were Parkerized.

Table 11
Follower Rod Identification Guide

Type	Markings	Length (inches)	Serial # Range	Comment
1A (Used with Compensating Spring)	C46014	6.8 x 0.18 dia.	Springfield circa serial #s 1-70,000 to 79,000. Winchester circa serial #s 100,001-102,000	See Figure 31. Drawing # on rod. Shoulder 2.42 inches from forked end. Short fork (slot 0.19 inch long), 14 vertical knurls, round behind shoulder
1B (Used with Compensating Spring)	None	6.8 x 0.18 dia.	Late in Springfield 1-70,000 to 79,000 & Winchester 100,001-102,000 serial # ranges	No drawing # on rod. Shoulder 2.42 inches from forked end. Short fork (slot 0.19 inch long), 14 vertical knurls, round behind shoulder
2 (Compensating Spring Eliminated)	None	6.8 x 0.20 dia.	Springfield circa serial #s 70,000-79,000 to 190,000	See Figure 32. Shoulder 0.915 inch from end of rod. Short fork (slot 0.19 inch long). Drawing # changed to C64331 to end of production but not marked, round behind shoulder
3A	None	6.8 x 0.215 width	Winchester circa serial #s 102,000-120,000.	See Figure 33. Forged in one piece, flat profile, 14 vertical knurls behind short fork (slot 0.19 inch long), unmarked

Table 11, cont.
Follower Rod Identification Guide

Type	Mark-ings	Length (inches)	Serial # Range	Comment
3B	None	6.8 x 0.215 width	Winchester from circa serial #s 120,000 intermittently to 2,533,060. Was not used between serial #s 1,600,001-1,640,000	Forged in one piece, flat profile, 14 vertical knurls behind short fork (slot 0.19 inch long), marked "CM," bevels on sides on lower fork prong
3C	None	6.8 x 0.215 width	Winchester circa serial #s 120,000-2,533,060. Was not used between serial #s 1,600,001-1,640,000	Forged in one piece, flat profile, 14 vertical knurls behind short fork (slot 0.19 inch long), marked "A," bevels on sides of lower fork prong
3D	None	6.8 x 0.215 width	Winchester serial #s 2,539,000-2,533,060. Was not used between serial #s 1,600,001-1,640,000	Forged in one piece, flat profile, 14 vertical knurls behind short fork (slot 0.19 inch long), marked with prick punch "•."
4	None	6.8 x 0.215 width	Springfield circa serial #s 190,000-2,500,000. See Figure 34.	Stamped from sheet metal. Short fork plate (slot 0.19 inch long) riveted. No marking

The M1 Garand

Table 11, cont.
Follower Rod Identification Guide

Type	Mark-ings	Length (inches)	Serial # Range	Comment
5	None	6.8 x 0.215 width	Springfield circa serial #s 2,500,000 to end of production. Winchester circa serial #s 2,500,000 to end of production; also in Win-13 production, serial #s 1,600,001-1,640,000. All International Harvester, Harrington & Richardson and refurbishment.	See Figure 35. Stamped from sheet metal. Long fork (slot 0.45 inch long) riveted. Grasping grooves eliminated. Springfield, IHC and H&R, no marking. Winchester with prick punch "○" or "A"

Operating Rod Catch

The operating rod catch drawing number was C46027. It engaged the operating rod when the rifle was in battery via a notch in its top surface which engaged a matching notch on the operating rod. When the bolt was opened, the operating rod catch disengaged from the operating rod and allowed the operating rod to compress the operating rod spring to power the bolt during the return portion of its cycle.

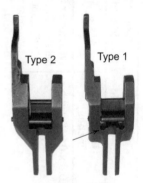

Type 2   Type 1

Figure 37

The second function was to apply pressure to the clip latch whenever the bolt was open to retain the en-bloc clip in place. On the last round fired, or when the clip latch was manually de-

78

pressed, the clip latch released the en-bloc clip and it was ejected. Two types of operating rod catches were manufactured. The shape of the operating rod catch was redesigned in late 1940-41. Early Type 1s to circa serial #700,000 were marked with the letter "O." The differences are shown in Figure 37 and Table 12.

Table 12 M1 Garand Operating Rod Catch Identification Guide			
Type	Right Fork (inches wide)	Left Fork (inches wide)	Width at Accelerator Rivet
1	0.08	0.08	0.73
2	0.10	0.07	0.79

Winchester manufactured Type 1 operating rod catches to circa serial #1,350,000. These are marked "CM," "A," punch-marked or are left unmarked. The Type 2 operating rod catch was used after and these are unmarked except for the punch mark. From circa serial #s 100,101-600,000, Winchester operating rod catches were left in the white; after, they were Parkerized. Blued examples also exist throughout the production run. Late Winchester operating catches can also be identified as they continued to use the rounded cuts in the "accelerator recess," refer to arrow in Figure 37.

International Harvester and Harrington & Richardson manufactured only the Type 2 operating rod catch. Early International Harvester operating rod catches were unmarked, later were marked "B, C, F, G, H or I." Harrington & Richardson operating rod catches were unmarked. All were Parkerized.

Accelerator
The accelerator was an "L"-shaped device secured with the accelerator rivet. The vertical stroke of the "L" was 0.290 inch high by 0.365 inch wide. The horizontal stroke was 0.385 inch long and 0.365 inch wide. See Figure 38. Two types of accelerators were developed. According to Major

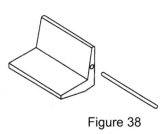

Figure 38

The M1 Garand

General Julian Hatcher (see Appendix K), the accelerator was changed slightly in 1940 to help eliminate the problem of the clip ejecting on the seventh round, rather than the eighth and last round. There are no discernible differences between the two types.

Springfield-manufactured accelerators were marked with the numeral "0" or "-0" until circa serial #240,000. After, they were unmarked. A very few accelerators have also been noted that are marked "A." Winchester accelerators may show a punch mark. International Harvester and Harrington & Richardson accelerators were unmarked. All were Parkerized.

Accelerator Rivet
The accelerator rivet was 0.845 inch long. It secured the accelerator in the operating rod catch. All were unmarked. Earliest rivets were left in the white, most World War II production was blued, and postwar production was Parkerized.

Follower Arm
The follower arm drawing number was B8869. It was 2.335 inches long and its body was 0.098 inch wide. The housing for the follower pin was 0.358 inch wide, was forked and bored with a hole 0.165 inch in diameter. The follower arm had cross-pins at the front and rear of the arm to which the follower assembly and follower rod assembly were attached. Early follower arms were blued, the balance Parkerized. All were marked or unmarked as detailed below.

Four variations were developed. They are identified by the type of, or lack of, bevel directly above the follower pin hole. See Figure 39. The arrow indicates the area from which the end views derive.

Type 1: The Type 1 follower arm had a single "triangular" bevel on the right side—0.10 inch wide for Springfield and 0.20 inch wide for Winchester-manufactured follower arms. Springfield used the Type 1 to circa serial #15,500; Winchester may have used them only in "educational" M1 Garands.

The M1 Garand

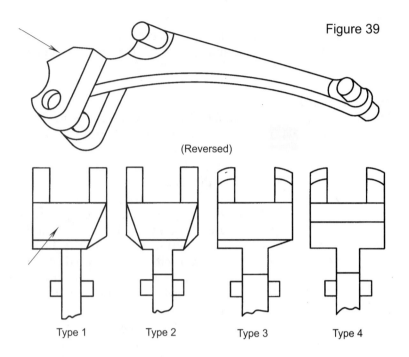

Figure 39

(Reversed)

Type 1   Type 2   Type 3   Type 4

Type 2: The Springfield-only-manufactured Type 2 follower arm had a double bevel, was stamped "B8869" and was in use from circa serial #s 15,500-33,000.

Type 3: The Type 3 follower arm had a single shallow bevel on the left side of the area above the pin hole. The follower arm pin lugs were rounded. It was used to circa serial #290,000.

Type 4: The Type 4 follower arm without a bevel but retaining the rounded follower arm pin lugs was used for the remainder of production. Springfield-manufactured follower arms may show a raised stamped letter "S" as well as various numbers which indicate the drop forge used to make them. These letters and numbers are often faint and appear as if polished. Post-World War II follower arms are not marked.

The majority of the Winchester follower arms used were Type 3s. They show Winchester's rough machining and inspector's punch mark. Many are also stamped "6," "8," or "9" to indicate the drop forge used. Postwar Springfield, International Harvester and Harrington & Richardson follower arms are the **Type 4** without a bevel and are unmarked.

Follower Arm Pin
The follower pin (drawing number A13667) was 1.240 inches long. It had a head 0.294 inch in diameter and its body was 0.154 inch in diameter. It held the operating rod catch, bullet guide and follower arm to the receiver, see Figure 40.

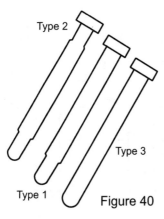

Type 2

Type 3

Type 1   Figure 40

Three types of follower pin were used. The **Type 1** had a rebate at the end only for 0.15 inch. The **Type 2** follower pins were rebated at both ends of the shank (0.07 inch long at the top and 0.15 inch long at the end) and were used by Springfield and Winchester during most of World War II. They were in the white or blued. **Type 3** follower arm pins had straight shafts with no rebates at either end. They were Parkerized and manufactured during the post-World War II period.

Follower
The follower (see Figure 41, overleaf) was actually an assembly composed of two pieces, the follower itself (A) and the cartridge slide (B). The follower's function was to apply pressure to the cartridges in the en-bloc clip to lift them into the path of the bolt, and the slide's function was to separate the two columns of cartridges. The follower "base" was 2.05 inches long by 1.02 inches wide. The "guide" was 1.857 inches long and its body was 0.144 inch wide.

Springfield produced two types of followers distinguished by the shape of the "tail." The **Type 1** followers had a narrow, winged tail. The wings were 1.22 inches wide, the tail 0.218 inch wide. Early Type 1 followers had vertical guide arms; later, they were raked forward at a 4-degree angle. The **Type 2** followers had a

The M1 Garand

tail 0.530 inch wide and guide arms raked 4 degrees forward. Winchester produced both types of followers which were used interchangeably and can only be distinguished from those of other manufacturers by a punch mark which appears on most but not all. WWII Springfield and Winchester followers are bright Parkerized, postwar, dull. The followers can further be broken down by the drawing number revision number stamped on the underside of the base's tail. International Harvester followers were the Type 2 and Parkerized. Some show a small stamped number or letter but no revision number. Harrington & Richardson also used the Type 2 follower, Parkerized and unmarked. The cartridge guide remained unchanged throughout production. See Table 13.

Table 13		
M1 Garand Follower Variations Identification Guide		
Type	**Marking**	**Circa Serial # Range**
Springfield		
1A	1	1-20,000
1B	2	20,001-34,500 to 39,000
1C	3	34,500-39,000 to 240,000
1D	None	34,500-39,000 to 240,000
2A	None	240,001-350,000
2B	8	350,001-710,000
2C	11	710,001-2,000,000
2D	12	2,000,001-3,650,000
2E	13	3,650,001-3,890,000
2F	None	Postwar Production
Winchester		
1D	CM (but not all)	100,001-2,340,000
2A	None	2,340,001-2,533,000 (*)
2C	11	2,340,001-2,533,000 (*)
2E	13	1,600,000-1,640,000
International Harvester		
2F	None	4,440,000-4,800,000 and 5,000,501-5,278,245

The M1 Garand

Table 13, cont. M1 Garand Follower Variations Identification Guide		
Type	Marking	Circa Serial # Range
Harrington & Richardson		
2F	None	4,660,001-4,800,000 and 5,488,247-5,793,847
(*) Winchester followers in this serial number range were either marked or unmarked		

NOTE: All followers manufactured for the M1 Garand were machined to shape. Investment cast followers are reproductions. No

investment castings were used on the M1 Garand. Investment casting can be distinguished by "seams" where the mold parts joined, by rounded corners and generally poor fit.

Bullet Guide
Determining which bullet guide was correct for a particular manufacturer of the M1 Garand and then the proper serial number range of use is difficult due to the many variations used.

Type 1   Type 2

Figure 41

Five different bullet guides were produced by Springfield and two different ones by Winchester, both with variations. International Harvester and Harrington & Richardson produced only one type, see Figure 42. Table 14 provides the differences by manufacturer and estimated serial number ranges. All bullet guides were Parkerized except for

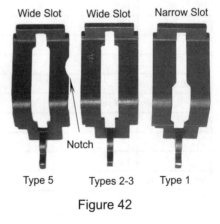

Figure 42

84

The M1 Garand

a very few early ones used on gas trap M1 rifles which were blued. They may show a drop-forge marking, i.e., "S/41," "S/49," etc.

The **Type 1** bullet guide had a narrow slot through the center 0.175 inch wide. All subsequent types had a wide slot measuring 0.300 inch. **Types 1A** through **3** were forged from solid steel and milled to shape. **Types 4** through **5** were stamped from sheet steel and the projection on the lower front through which the follower arm pin passed was riveted in place. The Type 5 bullet guide had a semicircular notch on the upper right side. The notch had a 0.25-inch radius. The Type 5 was developed after World War II when a small change was made in the Garand's timing and required a slightly altered accelerator height. The notch is used to identify this bullet guide, refer to Figure 42, arrow.

Table 14 Bullet Guide Identification Chart			
Type	**Marking**	**Circa Serial #**	**Comments**
Springfield			
1A	B-8875	1-9,999	Forged and milled. Narrow slot (1)
1B	B8875	10,000-35,000	Forged and milled. Narrow slot (1)
1C	B8875SA	35,000-65,000	Forged and milled. Narrow slot (1)
2A	B8875-1SA	65,000-300,000	Forged and milled. Wide slot (2)
2B	None	300,000-1,400,000	Forged and milled. Wide Slot (2)
3	None	1,400,000-2,850,000	Forged and milled. Wide Slot. Will have indentations on right and left sides at bottom 90-degree bend (2)
4	None	2,850,000-end of WW II production	Stamped steel. Wide slot. Top end folded back and formed (2)
5	None	4,200,000 to end of production	Stamped steel. Wide slot. Notch 0.25 inch in radius on upper left side. Postwar use to identify new accelerator height and change in timing (2)

The M1 Garand

Table 14, cont. Bullet Guide Identification Chart			
Type	**Marking**	**Circa Serial #**	**Comments**
Winchester			
1A	BB8875 W.R.A.	100,001-1,030,000	Forged and milled. Narrow slot (1)
1B	Punch Mark	1,030,000-1,065,000	Forged and milled. Narrow slot (1)
2A	CM	1,204,192-end of production	Forged and milled. Wide slot (2)
2B	A	1,204,192-2,533,000	Forged and milled. Wide slot (2)
2C	Punch Mark	1,204,192-2,533,000	Forged and milled. Wide slot (2)
2D	None or 8	1,600,000-1,640,000	Forged and milled. Wide slot (2)
International Harvester			
5	None	Entire production	Stamped steel. Wide slot. Notch 0.25 inch in radius on upper left side. Postwar use to identify new accelerator height and change in timing (2)
Harrington & Richardson Arms Company			
5	None	Entire production	Stamped steel. Wide slot. Notch 0.25 inch in radius on upper left side. Postwar use to identify new accelerator height and change in timing (2)
1 Narrow slot width 0.175 inch. 2 Wide slot width 0.300 inch.			

The M1 Garand

TRIGGER ASSEMBLY

The trigger assembly consisted of thirteen parts: 1) Trigger Housing, 2) Trigger Guard, 3) Trigger Guard Pin, 4) Trigger, 5) Trigger Pin, 6) Sear, 7) Sear Pin, 8) Hammer, 9) Hammer Spring Plunger, 10) Hammer Spring, 11) Hammer Spring Housing, 12) Safety and 13) Ejector Clip Spring. See Figure 43.

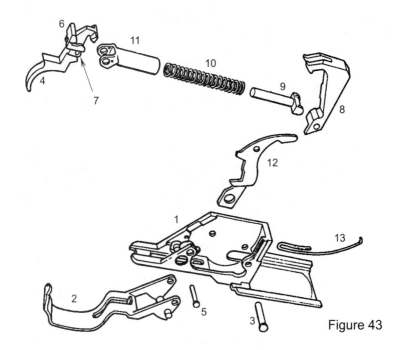

Figure 43

TRIGGER HOUSING

The trigger housing (drawing number D28290) held all twelve parts of the trigger assembly in proper relation to one another. Springfield manufactured thirteen variations of the trigger housing assembly, Winchester four and International Harvester and Harrington & Richardson one each, with two different markings, see Figure 44.

Types of trigger housings can be distinguished by the shape of the hole at the rear (round or "cloverleaf"), directly above the

The M1 Garand

trigger (1), by the drawing number stamped on the left side of the housing and by the size of the "pad," a trapezoidal raised section of metal (2) near the top of the housing. Early Springfield Type 1 (D28290) and all Winchester trigger guard housings types had an angled fillet (3) directly behind the clip spring attaching point. Type 3A

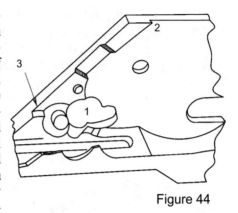

Figure 44

and later Springfield trigger housings had a rounded fillet, see Table 15, below.

There were two widths of pads (0.333 and 0.156 inch) manufactured by Springfield, one by Winchester (0.321 inch) and one each by International Harvester and Harrington & Richardson (0.205 inch). Pad sizes by drawing number revision and other characteristics of the trigger housing are listed in Table 15, below. The pad width was modified to allow the use of the Type 2 safety (drawing number C46015-6) described below. The final pad width determined by Springfield Armory and used to the end of production was nominally 0.156 ± 0.0156 inch. Actual sizes may vary depending on the machining process used and the care exercised. Early trigger pads were modified during rebuild procedures and may not show the exact sizes listed. If the trigger pad does not match one of the sizes listed, examine the trigger housing for indications of refinishing. Trigger pad dimensions were measured horizontally across their center as width was the critical measurement. The trigger pad shape was not important as long as it was thick enough to make contact with the left shoulder of the hammer during the firing cycle and at the same time, clear the safety. In effect, then, the pad served as an extra hammer stop.

The trigger housing was Parkerized. All manufacturers' trigger housings will show machine marks on inside, nonfriction surfaces. Winchester trigger housings show a rougher finish and individual

The M1 Garand

parts are usually marked with a punch. The majority of Winchester and Springfield trigger pads were modified to the nominal specified dimension of 0.156 ± 0.0156 inch width when rebuilt.

		Table 15	
		Trigger Housing Identification Guide	
Type	Marking	Circa Serial Number Range	Comments (1) (Dimensions in Inches)
Springfield			
1	D 28290	1-500	Round hole, no pad
2A	D 28290	501-38,000	Round hole, pad width 0.333
2B	D 2890 SA	38,001-75,000	Round hole, pad width 0.333
3A	D2890-1SA	75,001-90,000	Cloverleaf hole, pad width 0.156
3B	D2890-1-SA	90,001-160,000	Cloverleaf hole, pad width 0.156
4	D28290-2-SA	160,001-238,000	Cloverleaf hole, pad width 0.156
5	D28290-5-SA	238,001-744,000	Cloverleaf hole, pad width 0.156
6	D28290-7-SA	744,001-880,000	Cloverleaf hole, pad width 0.156 (0.136)
7	D28290-8-SA	880,001-1,010,000	Cloverleaf hole, pad width 0.156 (0.115)
8	D28290-12-SA	1,010,001-3,300,000	Cloverleaf hole, pad width 0.156 (0.145)
9	D28290-14-SA	3,300,001-3,450,000	Cloverleaf hole, pad width 0.156 (0.182)
10	D28290-16-SA	3,450,001-3,550,000	Cloverleaf hole, pad width 0.156
11	D28290-18-SA	3,550,001-3,890,000	Cloverleaf hole, pad width 0.156 (0.181)

The M1 Garand

		Table 15, cont. Trigger Housing Identification Guide	
Type	Marking	Circa Serial Number Range	Comments (1) (Dimensions in Inches)
12	6528290 SA	4,200,001-5,500,000	Cloverleaf hole, pad width 0.156 (0.156)
13	6528290-SA	5,500,001-6,099,905	Cloverleaf hole, pad width 0.156
Winchester			
1	D28290-W.R.A.	100,001-1,200,000	Round hole, pad width 0.321
2A	D28290-W.R.A.	1,200,001-2,533,000	Cloverleaf hole, pad width 0.321
2B	D28290W.R.A	1,300,000-2,533,000	Cloverleaf hole, pad width 0.321, mixed with Type 2A
3	D28290W.R.A./ C.M.	1,050,000-1,267,000	Cloverleaf hole, pad width 0.321
4	D28290-W.R.A.	1,600,000-1,640,000	Cloverleaf hole, pad width 0.321
International Harvester			
1A	IHC D6528290	4,400,000-4,660,000	Cloverleaf hole, pad width 0.205 (2), may be marked with letter code
1B	6528290 IHC	5,000,001-5,278,245	Cloverleaf hole, pad width 0.205 (2), may be marked with letter code
Harrington & Richardson Arms			
1	6528290 HRA N	All production	Cloverleaf hole, pad width 0.205 (2)

1 Pad width measurements were taken from actual trigger guard pads. The variations from the specified width of 0.156 ± 0.0156 inch are attributed to nonprecision cutting during rebuild procedures.
2 Pad widths in both IHC and HRA trigger housing were remarkably consistent in all examples measured.

The M1 Garand

Trigger Guard

The trigger guard (drawing number C46025) also causes collectors a great deal of confusion. There were two different types with ten variations in all. Trigger guards can be divided into two broad

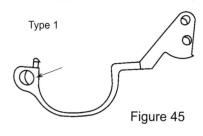

Type 1

Figure 45

types: **Type 1** were those milled from a solid piece of steel and **Type 2** were those stamped from sheet metal.

Type 1: The Type 1 "milled" trigger guard was 3.860 inches long overall with a maximum opening for the trigger of 1.565 inches wide. It had a 0.375-inch-diameter hole (1) at the rear, below the hook that latches the trigger guard to the trigger guard housing, see Figure 45, arrow.

Type 2: There were three variations of the Type 2 stamped trigger guard (see Figure 46) which can be identified by their latch: **Variation 2A** (1) had a horizontal cut across the base of the tab to form a ledge and **Variation 2B** (2) had a tab formed during the stamping process that was bent forward to serve as the latch.

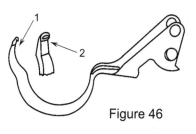

Figure 46

The Type 2 stamped trigger guard was 3.570 inches long overall with a maximum opening for the trigger of 1.395 inches wide.

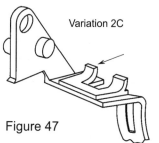

Variation 2C

Figure 47

The **Variation 2C** trigger guard had a horizontal cut across the base of the tab with the front of the guard surrounding the safety reinforced with an upward curving piece of steel spot-welded to the guard, see Figure 47, arrow.

This may have been used only for replacement trigger guards. All trigger guards were Parkerized. Table 16 presents the characteristics of each type.

The M1 Garand

		Table 16	
		Trigger Guard Identification Guide	
Type	**Marking**	**Circa Serial Number Range**	**Comments**
Springfield			
1A	Unknown	1-4	Milled, no rear hole
1B	C46025	5-16,000	Milled, concentric rings around rear hole
1C	C 46025	16,001- 40,000	Milled, concentric rings around rear hole
1D	C46025	40,001-80,000	Milled, rear hole, no concentric ring
1E	C46025-1SA	80,001-320,000	Milled, rear hole
1F	C46025-3-SA	320,001-425,000	Milled, rear hole, may show various inspectors' numbers or initials
1G	None	425,001-3,000,000	Milled, rear hole, may show various inspectors' numbers or initials
2A	None*	3,000,001-3,900,000	Stamped, milled hook
2B	None*	4,200,001-6,099,905	Stamped, tab hook
2C-not common	None*	Unknown	Stamped, milled hook, welded stop
Winchester			
1H	C 46025 W.R.A.	100,001-165,600	Milled, may show punch mark near drawing number, beveled corners on either side of drawing number
1I	C46025 W.R.A.	165,601 to end of production	Milled, may show punch marks near drawing number, no beveled corners and drawing number spaced out

Table 16, cont. Trigger Guard Identification Guide			
Type	Marking	Circa Serial Number Range	Comments
International Harvester			
2B	None	Entire production	Stamped, tab hook
Harrington & Richardson			
2B	None	Entire production	Stamped, tab hook
* Drawing number C7312631 assigned to Type 2 trigger guard. It was not stamped on the part.			

Trigger/Sear Assembly

There were two types of trigger/sear assemblies. The trigger had holes for the trigger pin and sear rivet. There were two types used.

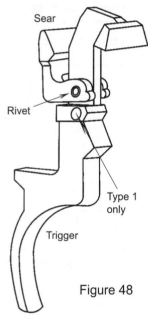

Figure 48

The **Type 1** trigger had a tooling hole 0.185 inch in diameter and 0.212 inch below the trigger pin hole. The **Type 2** trigger lacked this tooling hole. Winchester used both types but International Harvester and Harrington & Richardson used only the Type 2. The drawing number for the trigger/sear assembly was C46020. See Table 17.

The trigger and sear were separate parts but they were assembled at the factory and not intended to be disassembled. What appeared to be a pin holding the two parts together was actually a rivet, formed by upsetting the pin ends, see Figure 48.

Very early triggers in the gas port series were blued, but the majority of production were Parkerized. Most sears were Parkerized but blued sears are occasionally observed on early M1 Garands. Some Springfield triggers were marked with the drawing number

The M1 Garand

C46020 and the revision number on the left side flat above the finger piece as indicated in Table 17 below. Also, some will show the drop-forge "S" marking with various numbers.

Type	Marking	Serial Number Range	Comments
Table 17 **Trigger Identification Guide**			
Springfield			
1A	C46020	1-5,000	0.185-inch-diameter tooling hole
1B	C46020-1	5,000-9,000	0.185-inch-diameter tooling hole
1C	C46020-2	9,000-30,000	0.185-inch-diameter tooling hole
1D	None	30,000-80,000	0.185-inch-diameter tooling hole
2	None	80,000 to end of production	No tooling hole
Winchester			
1D	None	100,001-1,210,000	0.185-inch-diameter tooling hole
2A	None	1,200,000-1,333,700	No tooling hole
2B	None	1,333,700-2,533,060	No tooling hole, "A," punch mark
2A	None	1,600,000-1,640,000	No tooling hole
International Harvester			
2	None	Entire production	No tooling hole
Harrington & Richardson			
2	None	Entire production	No tooling hole

Winchester used the Type 1D trigger with the tooling hole 0.185 inch in diameter to circa serial #1,210,000. This tooling hole was used to hold the part in a fixture to mill the radii on the rear hooks. After, Winchester used the Type 2 trigger but the Type 1 trigger continued to be installed infrequently and usually with the marking "A." Winchester triggers without the tooling hole can also usually

The M1 Garand

be identified by the marking "A" stamped on the (right or left) flat and a punch mark. Early Winchester sears were marked with an "S," with and without serifs, on the rear flat. Late triggers were usually unmarked. Type 2A triggers were used in the Win-13 series (circa serial #s 1,600,000-1,640,000).

All post-World War II production triggers were unmarked and lacked the extra hole, no matter the manufacturer.

NOTE: Do not confuse the M14 rifle trigger assembly with the M1 Garand trigger. They are similar except that the M14 sear is 0.540 inch wide compared to the M1 sear which is 0.395 inch wide. The M14 trigger will not fit into an M1 stock. The M14 stock is routed on the right side for the selective-fire mechanism which used the larger sear.

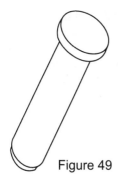

Figure 49

Trigger Pin

The trigger pin (drawing number A13669) attached the trigger/sear to the trigger guard housing, see Figure 49. It was 0.655 inch long and 0.095 inch in diameter. The trigger pin had a head 0.185 inch in diameter and was 0.06 inch thick. The end was cone-shaped. No changes were made to the trigger pin during the production of the M1 Garand by any manufacturer. As the trigger pin was a bearing surface, it was polished and finished. Trigger pins were usually blued but some original-appearing trigger pins appear to have been Parkerized. IHC trigger pins may show a punch mark on the head throughout production.

Sear Pin

The steel sear pin was 0.295 inch long by 0.08 inch in diameter. It was upset at both ends to hold the sear and trigger together. No changes were made to the sear pin. Like the trigger pin, there is probably no way to differentiate sear pins between the four manufacturers.

The M1 Garand

HAMMERS

The M1 Garand hammer (drawing number C46008) was 2.435 inches long overall, 0.510 inch wide at the widest point and 1.685 inches from front to back (beak to hooks), see Figure 50. Two hammer types with numerous variations were produced involving changes in the shape of the hammer hooks and a tooling hole near the top.

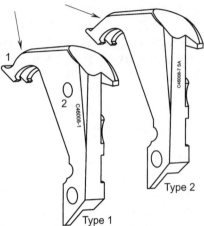

Figure 50

Prior to the start of World War II, four variations of the **Type 1** hammer with the early hooks (1) and tooling hole (2) were manufactured at Springfield. This "tooling hole" is labeled as such on the original design drawing D90237 (see S. Stoddard, Bibliography, Appendix K). During the war years, six variations of the **Type 2** hammer with the late hooks (compare the shape of the hooks at the arrows) and without the tooling hole were used followed by four postwar variations. Variations within types involved the placement of the drawing number.

Winchester manufactured only the **Type 1** hammer with the early hooks and tooling hole, in four variations involving the drawing number and inspection markings, and with and without the tooling hole. The drawing number is on the right side, reading bottom to top.

International Harvester and Harrington & Richardson used the **Type 2** hammer exclusively in four and two variations, respectively. International Harvester hammers may show a letter marking which may have indicated an acceptance check. Harrington and Richardson hammers for the M1 Garand are marked "HRA C5546008" or "HRA 5546008." See Table 18 for a complete listing of hammer types and variations by manufacturer.

NOTE 1: Wartime Springfield M1 Garand hammers show the drawing number marked on the front surface of the hammer read-

The M1 Garand

		Table 18 Hammer Identification Guide		
Type	Marking	Circa Serial Number Range	Comments
Springfield			
1A	C 46008	1-35,000	Drawing number on right side, early hooks, no tooling hole
1B	C 46008-1	35,000-55,000	Drawing number on right side, early hooks, tooling hole
1C	C46008-1	45,000-60,000	Drawing number on right side, early hooks, tooling hole
1D	C46008-1SA	60,000-65,000	Drawing number on right side, early hooks, tooling hole
2A	C46008-2SA	65,000-680,000	Drawing number either on right side or face, late hooks, no tooling hole
2B	C46008-2 SA	65,000-680,000	Drawing number either on right side or face, late hooks, no tooling hole
2C	C46008-3 SA	680,000-1,630,000	Drawing number on face, late hooks, no tooling hole
2D	C46008-5 SA	1,630,000-3,100,000	Drawing number on face, late hooks, no tooling hole
2E	C46008-7 SA	3,100,000-3,400,000	Drawing number on face, late hooks, no tooling hole
2F	C46008-8 SA	3,400,000-3,650,000	Drawing number on face, late hooks, no tooling hole
2G	C46008-9 SA	3,650,000-3,890,000	Drawing number on face, late hooks, no tooling hole
2H	SA C5546008	4,200,001-4,399,999	Drawing number on face, late hooks, no tooling hole
2I	SA D5546008	5,488,247-5,790,000	Drawing number on face, late hooks, no tooling hole
2J	SA 5546008	5,790,000-6,099,905	Drawing number on face, late hooks, no tooling hole

The M1 Garand

		Table 18, cont. Hammer Identification Guide		
Type	**Marking**	**Circa Serial Number Range**	**Comments**
Winchester			
1A	C46008-1W.R.A.	100,001-1,600,000; 1,640,000-2,400,000	Drawing number on right side, early hooks, with or without tooling hole
1B	C46008-1W.R.A.	159,000-160,000 and 2,400,000-2,530,000	Drawing number on right side, early hooks, "CM" marked, no tooling hole
1C	C46008-1W.R.A.	2,400,000-2,530,000	Drawing number on right side, early hooks, "A" marked, but no tooling hole
1D	C4-6008-1W.R.A.	2,400,000-2,530,000	Drawing number on right side, early hooks, no tooling hole
1B	C-46008-1W.R.A.	1,600,000-1,640,000	Drawing number on right side, early hooks, no tooling hole
International Harvester			
2A	C-5546008 IHC	4,440,000-4,500,000	Drawing number on face, late hooks, no tooling hole
2B	IHC C5546008	4,500,000-5,010,000	Drawing number on face, early hooks, no tooling hole
2C	5546008IHC	5,010,000-5,278,245	Drawing number on face, early hooks, no tooling hole
2D	5546008IHC	5,010,000-5,278,245	Drawing number on face, early hooks, letter stamped above drawing number, no tooling hole
Harrington & Richardson			
2A	HRA C5546008	4,660,000-4,800,000	Drawing number on face, early hooks, no tooling hole

The M1 Garand

Table 18, cont. Hammer Identification Guide			
Type	Marking	Circa Serial Number Range	Comments
2B	HRA 5546008	5,488,247-5,793,847	Drawing number on face, early hooks, no tooling hole. NOTE: other numbers on HRA hammers signify M14 production

ing from bottom to top, i.e., with the letters and numbers oriented to the right. Postwar hammers are the reverse, i.e., with the letters and numbers oriented to the left.

NOTE 2: Harrington & Richardson M14 hammers were made to the same dimensions as the M1 Garand hammer but will be marked "5546008 HRA" or "5546008 HR."

Hammer Spring Plunger

Two types of hammer spring plungers were manufactured for the M1 Garand under the drawing number B8880, see Figure 51. The **Type 1** hammer plunger manufactured by Springfield was in use throughout World War II production.

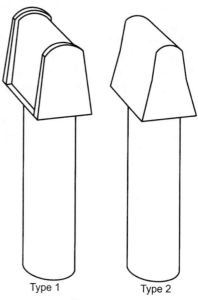

Type 1   Type 2

Figure 51

Type 2 hammer plunger production began at circa serial #2,700,000. They were used concurrently with Type 1 hammer plungers to the end of wartime production at circa serial #3,890,000. Hammer plungers were routinely Parkerized although occasionally, blued hammer plungers are observed. These are thought to be early production. Hammer plungers are unmarked.

Type 1 hammer plungers were 1.542 inches long. The head with protruding sides or wings was 0.459 inch wide.

Type 2 hammer plungers were 1.50 inches long. Their heads lacked the protruding sides or wings and were 0.40 inch wide. The hammer plunger shaft was 1.250 inches long and 0.215 inch in diameter. Several variations of this "wingless" hammer plunger will be noted, distinguished by somewhat rounded top edges.

Winchester also manufactured both types of hammer plungers. The **Type 1** hammer plunger was in use throughout Winchester production. Winchester **Type 2** hammer plunger production started at circa serial #s 2,340,000-2,380,000. They were used concurrently with Type 1 hammer plungers to the end of production. This may have resulted from excess inventory situations rather than a deliberate plan. Type 2 Winchester hammer spring plungers were ground flat on the sides of the head while Springfield-made hammer spring plungers have rounded sides.

Hammer plungers used in postwar production of M1 Garands by Springfield, International Harvester and Harrington & Richardson were the **Type 2s**. They were unmarked and cannot be identified by manufacturer.

Hammer Spring

The hammer spring (drawing number B8887) was made of steel wire 0.062 inch in diameter. It had 20 coils. Some hammer springs were blued, possibly from the tempering process, but most appear to have been white. Some lightly Parkerized hammer

Figure 52

springs have been noted but these are probably the result of the refinishing during a rebuilding process. See Figure 52.

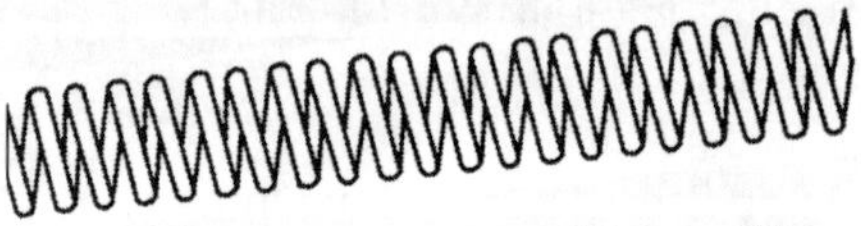

The M1 Garand

Hammer Spring Housing
The hammer spring housing (drawing number B8883) was 1.605 inches long overall. The wing guides at the rear were 0.427 inch wide by 0.30 inch long. Each wing guide had two holes, one 0.165 inch in diameter and the other 0.056 inch in diameter. The larger hole allowed the trigger pin to pass through.

The barrel which contained the hammer spring was 0.410 inch in diameter and 1.245 inches long. It had a slot with rounded ends 0.970 inch long by 0.256 inch wide cut into its right side to clear the safety, see Figure 53, arrow 1.

Two types of hammer spring housing were made and all were un-marked—although Winchester hammer spring housings may show a punch mark. To circa serial #740,000, the hammer spring housing was left unfinished; after, they were blued or Parkerized.

Figure 53

Type 1 hammer spring housing can be identified by the 5-degree rounded bevel at the ends of the safety slot. They were used on early Springfield gas trap M1s, and on Winchester M1s to circa serial #2,500,000.

Type 2 hammer spring housings were used by Springfield on all gas port rifles to the end of World War II production. A change dated 6/17/44 on design drawing B8883 (originally dated 6/27/38) and used by Winchester allowed a 45-degree slanted cut to replace the 5-degree bevel (arrow 2). The authors caution, though, that have been unable to identify any Type 2 hammer spring housings in Winchester M1 Garands (see Stoddard, Bibliography, Appendix K). The Type 2 was also used on all post-World War II production M1 Garands.

Safety
Three types of M1 Garand safety (drawing number C46015) were manufactured—with numerous subvariations. The Type 1 safety had a long, flat upper side and top, See Figure 54 (1). The Type 2 had a rounded upper side and no tooling hole while the Type 3 had a rounded upper side (2) and tooling hole (3) added.

The M1 Garand

All safeties were stamped from sheet metal and all were Parkerized. Table 19 lists known variations and their serial number range. Pay close attention to the drawing numbers. Safeties stamped "SA" were manufactured for the M14 rifle but may have been installed in M1 Garands refurbished in the late 1960s.

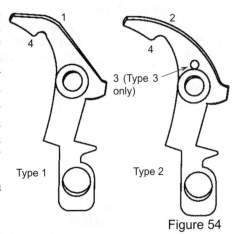

Figure 54

NOTE: Billy Pyle, editor of the *Garand Stand Report*, warns that the weakest area of the safety is the nose, which has a tendency to break off at the hammer lock area (refer to Figure 54, 4). To determine if the hammer lock is broken or damaged without removing it from the trigger guard, first make certain that the rifle is empty, then pull the trigger to lower the hammer. Put the safety on. If it goes on, the hammer lock is broken. If it does not, the hammer lock is sound. Also, be aware that reproduction safeties are now on the market. Since these were probably not made to military specifications, they may be unsafe.

Ejector Clip

The ejector clip (C46018) was a flat wire spring with round sections, positioned in the trigger guard to provide tension on the safety and the bottom of the en-bloc clip. When the last round was fired, the spring ejected the clip. No changes were made to the ejector clip during its production by any manufacturer. See Figure 55.

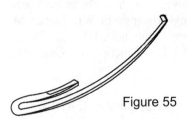

Figure 55

The ejector clip spring was 2.810 inches long overall. The front and rear portions of the spring were round and 0.085 inch in diameter. The flattened portions of the spring were 0.125 inch wide.

The M1 Garand

The front of the spring was bent to the left for 0.305 inch. Early ejector clip springs were blued. Late ejector clip springs were Parkerized.

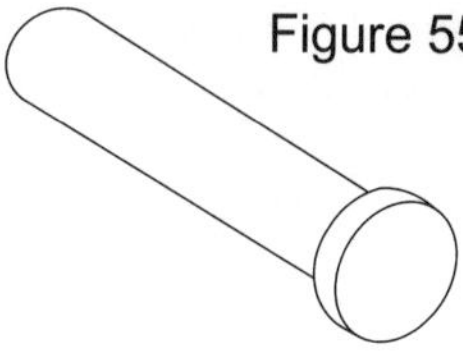

Figure 55A

Hammer Pin
The hammer rotated on the hammer pin (drawing number A13668) which also served to secure the trigger guard in the trigger guard housing. It was 0.205 inch in diameter and 0.835 inch long. The head was 0.225 inch in diameter and 0.05 inch high, see Figure 55A.

Table 19 Safety Identification Guide			
Type	Markings	Circa Serial Number Range	Comments
Springfield			
1A	None	1-80, 81-300	Flat upper side and top, no drawing number marked
1B	C 46015	301-2,000	Flat upper side and top
1C	C 46015-1	2,001-5,000	Flat upper side and top
1D	C 46015-3	5,001-15,000	Flat upper side and top
1E	C 46015-4	15,001-34,000	Flat upper side and top
1F	C 46015-4SA	34,001-75,000	Flat upper side and top
2*	C46015-6SA	75,001-290,000	Rounded upper side and top, no tooling hole
3A*	C46015-6SA	290,001-750,000	Rounded upper side and top, 0.12-inch-diameter tooling hole
3B	C46015-9SA	750,001-2,000,000	Rounded upper side and top, tooling hole

The M1 Garand

Table 19, cont. Safety Identification Guide			
Type	**Markings**	**Circa Serial Number Range**	**Comments**
3C	SA-11 (All) SA-11 (1950s)	2,000,001 to end of production	Rounded upper side and top. Numerous variations on the SA-11 marking have been observed, including hand-stamped hyphens; tooling hole
Winchester			
1G	C46015-4 W.R.A.	100,001-112,500	Flat upper side and top, drawing number stamped on right side of the upper arm
1H	C46015-4-W.R.A.	112,500-2,533,000	Flat upper side and top, drawing number stamped on lower left side
1I	W.R.A.-1	2,350,000-2,533,000 1,600,000-1,640,000	Flat upper side and top, drawing number W.R.A.-1 stamped on lower left side
International Harvester			
3D	IHC	4,400,000-4,600,000	Marked on right side, tooling hole
3E	F	5,000,001-5,500,000	Marked on right side (subcontracted part), tooling hole
Harrington & Richardson			
3F	HRA	Entire production	Marked on right side. May show inspector's initial preceding "HRA." Those marked "5546015 HRA" or "5546015 H&R" are M14 safeties; tooling hole

The M1 Garand

GAS CYLINDER ASSEMBLY

Two different gas cylinders were used on M1 Garand rifles. The **Type 1** was the so-called "gas trap" gas cylinder. An attached cap covered the muzzle of the barrel. Between the muzzle and the gas cylinder plug was a slight gap into which escaped a certain amount of the propellant gas that drove the bullet through the barrel. The gas passed through this gap into the gas cylinder below and drove the operating rod back which, in turn, cycled the bolt. There were three drawbacks to the gas trap system: 1) carbon deposits developed inside the muzzle cap which altered the power of the mechanism, 2) muzzle cap and gas cylinder were difficult to clean because of carbon buildup and 3) the muzzle cap did not provide a firm support for the bayonet.

To eliminate these problems, the **Type 2** gas system was developed, the so-called "gas port" gas cylinder. A gas vent or port 0.0805 inch in diameter was drilled in the bottom of the barrel and the muzzle cap was eliminated. Three splines were also cut to support the gas cylinder as opposed to the single spline in the gas trap design. As the bullet passed the port, a certain amount of the expanding gases rushed through the hole at high velocity and impacted directly against the face of the operating rod—known as the piston—driving it to the rear. Carbon deposits could not develop in the barrel vent because of velocity of the gas and this eliminated cleaning difficulties.

And since the bayonet now mounted directly on the firm support of the barrel, that problem disappeared as well. The change to the new gas system was authorized on October 26, 1939, and placed into production in July 1940 at circa serial #50,000. The first of the gas port M1 Garands were in the hands of the troops later that year.

All gas cylinders were made of stainless steel; they were not Parkerized but were chemically blackened from the start of production, whether gas trap or gas port. Gas cylinders that were refurbished and in need of re-blackening were painted with black paint, which was baked on. This process occurred during and after World War II as detailed in TM9-1275, June 1947 (see Appendix K, Bibliography).

105

The M1 Garand

GAS CYLINDER, TYPE 1 (GAS TRAP M1)

The gas trap cylinder drawing number was D28289. The assembly consisted of the gas cylinder, gas cylinder plug and gas cylinder plug screw. The front sight was mounted on the gas cylinder. See Figure 56.

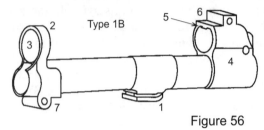

Figure 56

The gas trap gas cylinder was 4.95 inches long overall. It was wider at the front (0.682 inch) than at the middle or rear (0.665 inch). The bayonet mount (1) was centered 1.85 inches from the rear. The rear ring (2) was 0.368 inch wide. The bore (3) for the barrel was 0.570 inch in diameter. The front ring (4) was 1.595 inches long and it had a single spline (5) machined into the interior of the ring at the 12 o'clock position. The spline was 0.120 inch wide, 0.040 inch thick and 0.840 inch long. The top of the front ring had a dovetail (6) for the front sight 0.40 inch wide by 0.70 inch long. The ring itself was 0.50 inch wide and 0.765 inch long.

The stacking swivel assembly was attached to both types of gas cylinders via a boss (7) at the rear. The boss had a small shelf ahead of it which made it 0.435 inch wide. The shelf was 0.185 inch high. The boss was drilled 0.190 inch in diameter for the stacking swivel screw.

Three Type 1 gas cylinder variations were manufactured by the Springfield Armory for the gas trap Garand (drawing number D28289). The **Type 1A** gas cylinder was marked with the drawing number (D28289) on the rear ring. It had narrow "flutes" machined in the area below the rear sight base to serve as lightening cuts. It was used to circa serial #25,000. The **Type 1B** gas cylinder lacked both the drawing number and flutes and was used to circa serial #32,000. The **Type 1C** gas cylinder was marked with the drawing number (D-28289-1) but lacked the flutes and

The M1 Garand

was used to the end of the gas trap M1 Garand production at circa serial #50,000. See also Table 20, below.

NOTE: One gas trap M1 Garand gas cylinder (#15,070) observed at the Cody Firearms Museum, Buffalo Bill Historical Center, Cody, Wyoming, had a "1" stamped directly behind the front sight and the number "0" on the gas plug directly forward of the front sight. Other gas trap plugs through the serial #50,000 range have also been reported with and without the number "0."

GAS CYLINDER, TYPE 2 (GAS PORT M1)

The **Type 2** gas cylinder drawing number was D35449. The gas cylinder assembly for the gas port M1 Garand consisted of the gas cylinder, gas cylinder lock and gas cylinder lock nut. The front sight was mounted on the gas cylinder assembly, see Figure 57.

Two Type 2 variations of the gas port gas cylinder were manufactured by both Springfield and Winchester. The difference between the two lay in the width of the sight base. Also, Winchester gas cylinders differ most noticeably from those made by Springfield in that the Winchester rear ring does not have a machined flat on top, but is round.

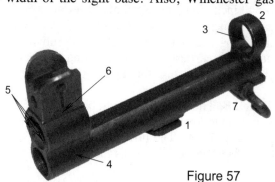

Figure 57

NOTE: A hand-written note in red pencil dated 3/1/40 was discovered on drawing D35449 by S. Stoddard, then Assistant Curator of the Cody Firearms Museum, which read: "This flat is not mandatory and may be omitted from W.R.A. production. R.E.F. SA 380/1444 G-2840." See Stoddard, Bibliography, Appendix K.

The Type 2 series gas port gas cylinders were 5.165 inches long overall with an outside diameter of 0.670 inch. The bayonet mount (1) was centered 2.40 inches from the rear. The rear ring (2) was

The M1 Garand

1.460 inches high, 0.90 inch wide and 0.09 inch thick at the sides and 0.60 inch thick at the top. The bore (3) for the barrel was 0.590 inch in diameter. The front ring (4) was 0.840 inch long and it had three splines (5) machined into the interior of the ring at the 12, 5 and 7 o'clock positions. The splines were 0.120 inch wide, 0.040 inch thick and 0.840 inch long. The top of the front ring was machined into a dovetail mount (6) for the front sight. The interior of the gas cylinder was 0.532 inch.

The stacking swivel was fitted into a lug (7) machined onto the rear bottom surface of the gas cylinder. The lug was 0.420 inch wide by 0.356 inch in diameter. The hole for the stacking swivel was 0.195 inch in diameter. The lug was centered 0.510 inch from the rear of the gas cylinder.

The **Type 2** series of gas ports are chiefly distinguished by the width of the front sight base. Three widths were used.

Type 2A: The narrow front sight base was 0.50 inch wide and 0.840 inch long circa Springfield serial #s 50,001-315,000 and circa Winchester serial #s 100,001-125,000. The dovetail was 0.340 inch long and 0.10 inch high. Two subvariations were manufactured, the earliest with the drawing number marked on the right side of the rear ring, the later without the drawing number.

Type 2B: The wide front sight base was 0.50 inch wide and 0.840 inch long to Springfield serial #1,600,000 and circa Winchester serial #2,350,000. The dovetail remained 0.340 inch long and 0.10 inch high but the width was increased to 0.575-0.580 inch.

Type 2C: Both Springfield and Winchester increased the width of the sight base to 0.570-0.580 inch wide. Otherwise, they are the identical to the Type 2B.

International Harvester and Harrington & Richardson used the **Type 2C** gas cylinder but with a sight base width of 0.575-0.582 inch.

Front Sight Base Modifications
As noted above, the width of the front sight base was increased twice to allow more rifles to be accepted. Originally, the front

The M1 Garand

sight was mounted in a fixed position and the rear sight could only be moved three "clicks" right or left to zero the rifle for acceptance. This made for a high rejection rate based on an inability to "sight-in." By establishing a wide base on which the front sight could be moved to the left or right until the rifle was "zeroed," the rejection rate dropped and more M1 Garands were made available for combat.

The collector will encounter gas port gas cylinders with saw cuts across the front sight platform. It was discovered during World War II that the tolerances to which the gas port gas cylinders were made were somewhat excessive, permitting both gas leakage and front sight movement.

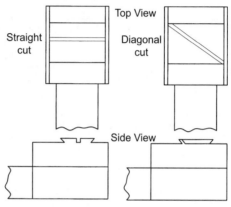

Figure 58

Specifications were tightened but until all manufacturing problems were worked out, a series of Field Service Modification Work Orders was issued. Armorers were instructed to cut a narrow groove straight across the sight platform dovetail and the upper surface of the gas cylinder front ring so that when the front sight screw was tightened down, the front of the gas cylinder was also tightened to the barrel. See Figure 58.

From May 27, 1943 to October 14, 1943, the saw cut width was set at 0.050 inch. From October 14, 1943 to December 20, 1943, it was reduced to 0.035 inch and applied only to rifles in service if the rifle front sight motion exceeded 0.015 inch. For rifles undergoing overhaul, if the front sight movement exceeded 0.007 inch, then the saw cut was also made. After March 1, 1944, the saw cut was changed from "straight across" to "diagonally across," again not exceeding 0.035 inch. The practice was ended on May 8, 1945. As of September 15, 1953, gas cylinders with saw cuts could only be used if the cut had been made diagonally. All cross-cut gas cylinders were discarded.

The M1 Garand

<table>
<tr><td colspan="4">**Table 20**
Gas Cylinder Identification Guide</td></tr>
<tr><th>Type</th><th>Marking</th><th>Serial Number Range</th><th>Comments</th></tr>
<tr><td colspan="4">**Springfield—Gas Trap Gas Cylinder**</td></tr>
<tr><td>1A</td><td>D28289, top of rear ring</td><td>81-25,000</td><td>Flutes, 0.50-inch front sight platform, flat top on rear ring</td></tr>
<tr><td>1B</td><td>Unmarked</td><td>25,001-32,000</td><td>No flutes, 0.50-inch front sight platform, flat top on rear ring</td></tr>
<tr><td>1C</td><td>D-28289-1, top of rear ring</td><td>32,001-50,000</td><td>No flutes, 0.50-inch front sight platform, flat top on rear ring</td></tr>
<tr><td colspan="4">**Springfield—Gas Port Gas Cylinder**</td></tr>
<tr><td>2A</td><td>D-35449-SA, right side of rear ring</td><td>50,001-315,000</td><td>0.50-inch front sight platform, flat top on rear ring</td></tr>
<tr><td>2B</td><td>Unmarked</td><td>315,001-1,600,000</td><td>0.50-inch front sight platform, flat top on rear ring</td></tr>
<tr><td>2C</td><td>Unmarked</td><td>1,600,001 to end of M1 Garand production</td><td>0.575-0.580-inch front sight platform, flat top on rear ring</td></tr>
<tr><td colspan="4">**Winchester—Gas Port Gas Cylinder**</td></tr>
<tr><td>2D</td><td>D35449W.R.A. right side of rear ring</td><td>100,001-125,000</td><td>0.50-inch front sight platform, no flat top on rear ring</td></tr>
<tr><td>2B</td><td>Unmarked</td><td>125,001-1,600,000 and 125,001-2,350,000</td><td>0.50-inch front sight platform, no flat top on rear ring</td></tr>
<tr><td>2C</td><td>Unmarked</td><td>2,350,001-2,533,060 and 1,600,001-1,640,000</td><td>0.575-0.580-inch front sight platform, no flat top on rear ring</td></tr>
<tr><td colspan="4">International Harvester—Springfield Type 2C, 0.575-0.582-inch wide front sight platform; flat top on rear ring; may show single numbers or letters which may be inspector's or machinist's marks, otherwise usually unmarked.</td></tr>
</table>

The M1 Garand

Table 20, cont. Gas Cylinder Identification Guide			
Type	Marking	Serial Number Range	Comments
Harrington & Richardson—Springfield Type 2C, 0.575-0.582-inch wide front sight platform; flat top on rear ring; may show single numbers or letters which may be inspector's or machinist's marks, otherwise usually unmarked.			

Gas Cylinder Plug

The gas cylinder plug (drawing number B8876) was used only on the gas trap M1 Garands, see Figure 59. It attached to the front of the gas cylinder with twin rails on either side that slid into the matching tracks on the front inside of the gas cylinder and was secured in place with a screw that penetrated from the right side. When the bullet left the barrel, some of the expanding gases behind it flowed down into the gap between the gas cylinder plug and the barrel and struck the head of the gas piston to drive it back.

Figure 59

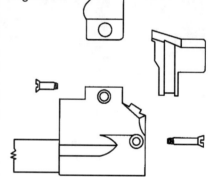

The two types of gas cylinder plug were produced for the gas trap system and can be differentiated by a small hole below the muzzle in the Type 1 which was lacking in the Type 2.

Four variations of markings have been observed: the earliest production was marked with the drawing number on the right side, "B8876." The second type was marked "B-8876." The third type was marked "0" or "-0," usually on the top surface. The fourth type was unmarked. Surviving samples observed were too few to give an estimate of serial number ranges.

The M1 Garand

Gas Cylinder Lock

The gas cylinder lock (drawing number B147426) was used to hold the gas cylinder in place on the gas port barrel, see Figure 60. It was shaped like a figure 8. The top of the "8" was 0.733 inch in diameter, the bottom 0.694 inch in diameter. A shelf 0.280 inch long by 0.620 inch wide projected from the front, top of the "8" to add extra support (A). The interior of the upper part of the "8" was threaded to screw onto the barrel. The lower bore of the "8" was left unthreaded for the gas cylinder lock screw to pass through.

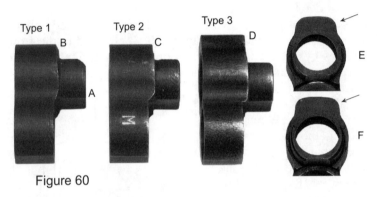

Figure 60

The gas cylinder lock was made of stainless steel and could not be blued, Parkerized or black oxide finished; instead, it was chemically blackened during production. Those requiring refinishing were painted with flat black enamel if the chemical finish was not available.

Three types of gas cylinder locks were developed. Although unmarked, they are easily recognized: **Type 1** upper front face was chamfered (B), **Type 2** lacked the chamfer and was marked "M" on the right lower side, and **Type 3** lacked the chamfer (C) and the marking and had a hump 0.220 inch high (D).

Harrington & Richardson gas cylinder locks have a lower hump (E) 0.210 inch high, and appear narrower than the hump on Springfield or IHC gas cylinder locks (F). This is due to a larger edge radius at the top sides of the hump (arrows).

The M1 Garand

NOTE: The "M" marking on the Type 2 Gas Cylinder lock denoted that it was hardened and was to be used with the M7 grenade launcher. Eventually, all M1 Garands were built with the Type 2 gas cylinder lock by the end of World War II.

Type	Part Number	Serial Number Range	Comments
Table 21 **Gas Cylinder Lock Identification Guide**			
Springfield			
1	B147426, unmarked	50,000-3,592,361	Front face chamfered, no hump, 1.225-1.335 inches high overall
2	B147426, unmarked	3,592,361-3,890,000	Front face not chamfered, no hump, hardened, most often marked "M"
3A	B147426, unmarked	4,200,000-4,250,000 to end of production	Front face not chamfered, hardened, 0.220-inch-high hump on top surface, no markings, may show punch mark from hardness testing, 1.455 inches high overall
3B	B147426	4,660,001 to end of production	Low hump with rounded edges
Winchester — Type 1 unmarked except for punch mark and machine marks around face			
International Harvester — Type 3A unmarked, high hump			
Harrington & Richardson — Type 3B, unmarked, low hump			

Gas Cylinder Lock Screw

Three major types of the gas cylinder lock screws were developed and are described in Table 22 and Figure 61. All were made of stainless steel and as with the gas cylinder and gas cylinder lock, could not be Parkerized or black oxide finished. They were originally chemically blackened and if refinished at a later date, painted with flat black enamel if the chemical finish was not available.

The M1 Garand

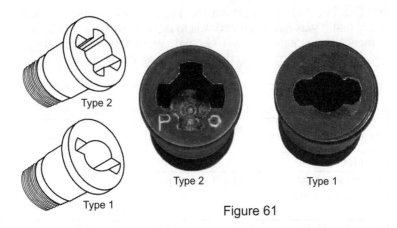

Type 2

Type 1

Type 2   Type 1

Figure 61

Type 1 (drawing number B147428) was characterized by a single cross-wise slot for the screwdriver blade on the M3 combination tool. It was milled from a solid piece of stainless steel and had fourteen threads per inch.

Type 2 (drawing number B147851) had a "non-return valve" installed to permit the use of the M7 grenade launcher. It was characterized by a "cross-shaped" screwdriver slot with a round hole in the center, 0.280 inch in diameter. When the grenade launcher was mounted on the barrel, a stud slid into the center hole of the gas cylinder lock and depressed the valve. This allowed a certain amount of gas to escape from the gas cylinder, thus reducing the pressure against the piston to prevent the rear of the bolt from hammering and ultimately damaging the receiver. When a standard ball cartridge was next fired, the gas pressure closed the valve. Two variations of this valve were developed: **Type 2A** had a carbon steel spring which tended to corrode and was replaced by the **Type 2B** which had a stainless steel spring and was marked "S." Both Types 2A and 2B were withdrawn from service starting in early 1944.

Type 3 (drawing number B7310079) was designed with a "poppet valve" which opened when the grenade launcher stud was inserted, and closed when it was removed. It entered service in early 1944 and also had the "cross-shaped" screwdriver slot with center hole for the grenade launcher stud. These are marked "P" for "poppet

114

Table 22 Gas Cylinder Lock Screw Identification Guide			
Type	Markings (Drawing Number)	Serial Number Range	Comments
Springfield			
1	Unmarked (B147428)	50,000 -2,500,000	Solid, single slot
2	S (B147851)	1,470,000- 2,500,000	Non-return valve, cross-shaped slot, may show manufacturer code, issued with M7 Grenade Launcher
3	Various initials or symbols* (B7310079)	2,500,000-end of production	Return (poppet) valve, cross-shaped slot, "P" mark, also may show manufacturer code
Winchester			
1	Unmarked	100,001-165,000 and 1,200,000- 2,533,000	Solid, single slot, may show punch mark or circular machine marks on face
3	P, O (B7310079)	1,600,000- 1,640,000	Return (poppet) valve, may show "P" marked and "O" or "hexagon" manufacturer code
International Harvester — Type 3, will be marked with manufacturer code "IHC" or "IHC NHC"			
Harrington & Richardson — Type 3, will be marked with manufacturer code "HRA" or "HRA O"			
* Springfield markings observed indicating manufacture by a subcontractor are: B S, O, P, small hexagon P, large hexagon P, P with crescent moon, PBV, P O, P X, P▲, P▲, T, T A, T O, T PAX, octagon			

valve." A note on the original design drawing dated 3/24/44 states that it would be applied after the "application of a load test."

Springfield Armory records indicate that the Type 1 solid gas cylinder lock screw was manufactured all through World War II,

The M1 Garand

concurrently with either the Type 2 or Type 3. Postwar, only the Type 3 was manufactured. All M1 Garands manufactured after January 1944 had the Type 3 (Poppet Valve) installed. Springfield gas cylinder lock valve screws generally had a smooth face and square edges at the periphery.

Winchester manufactured the Type 1 single slot, solid gas cylinder lock screw exclusively, except for the Win-13 rifles in the 1,600,000-1,640,000 serial number range produced in 1945 which used the Type 3 cylinder lock screw, marked with a "P," "O" or a hexagon. Winchester Type 1 gas cylinder lock screws show concentric machining rings around the screwdriver slot and rounded edges at the periphery. Winchester gas cylinder poppet lock screws were manufactured by subcontractors.

International Harvester used only Type 3 gas cylinder valve lock screws, most of which were marked "IHC" or "IHC NHC."

Harrington & Richardson gas cylinder valve lock screws were also Type 3s and were marked "HRA" or "HRA O."

The variety of markings observed to date include: "B S," "HRA," "HRA O," "IHC O," "NHC," "NHC IHC," "O," "P," "P" with a small hexagon, "P" with a large hexagon, "P" with a crescent moon, "PBV," "P O," "P X," "P ▴," "P ▲," "T," "T A," "T O," "T PAX," or an octagon. The "O" designation is known to stand for the subcontractor, The Henry Owen Company.

FRONT SIGHT ASSEMBLY
The front sight assembly consisted of the front sight, front sight screw and front sight cap. See Figure 62.

Front Sight
Three types of front sights were manufactured. The **Type 1** front sight was a single blade without guards used only on the preproduction M1 Garands. The **Type 2** front sight (drawing number B8882) was used on the Gas Trap M1 Garands to circa serial

The M1 Garand

#50,000 and was manufactured in two variations.

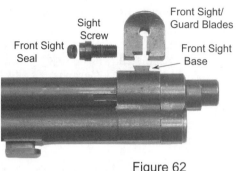

Figure 62

Type 2A had straight guard blades and **Type 2B** had flared guard blades. The change was made early in production as soldiers complained of mistaking one of the straight guard blades for the sight itself. A number of drawing number revisions will be observed but the scarcity of original specimens made it impossible to quantify these, see Figure 63.

Side View

Figure 63

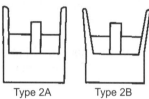

Type 2A   Type 2B

The gas trap M1 Garand front sight guard blades were not as rounded as the later Type 3. The curve of the guard blade from back to front formed one-quarter of a circle from the 9 to the 2 o'clock position. The front sight did not have a vertical slot.

When the gas port system replaced the gas trap system at circa serial #50,000, the **Type 3** front sight came into use and the drawing number was changed to B147427. It was evenly rounded across the top, had a vertical slit ending in a hole 0.2 inch in diameter, and flared guard blades. See Figure 64. Three variations have been observed:

Side View

Type 3A

Type 3B   Type 3C

Figure 64

The M1 Garand

Type 3A manufactured by Springfield and Harrington & Richardson measured between 0.625 to 0.687 inch across the top of the guard blades. Where Springfield was concerned, the smaller width was generally associated with World War II and the larger with the post-World War II M1 Garands.

Type 3B were manufactured by Winchester and measured 0.812 inch across the guard blades. They almost always show a punch mark.

Type 3C were manufactured by International Harvester and measured 0.875 inch across the guard blades. IHC manufactured the widest sight.

Front Sight Screw

Three types of screws were used to hold the front sight in place on the M1 Garand. The **Type 1** was a slotted screw used on the gas trap M1 Garands.

The **Type 2** was used on the gas port M1s and was a socket or "Allen" head screw. It was 0.754 inch long overall, had a diameter of 0.245 inch and a 3/16 inch socket in the head. See Figure 65.

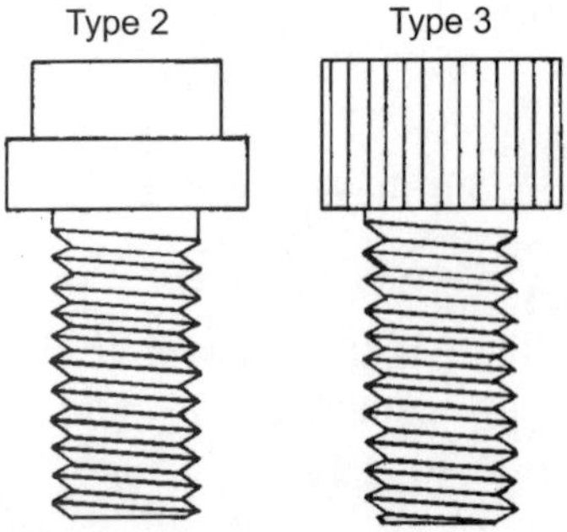

Type 2   Type 3

Figure 65

The Type 2 front sight screw had a rebated head; the full diameter of the head was 0.361 inch in diameter while the rebated upper portion was 0.255 inch in diameter. This screw was used in conjunction with the front sight screw seal. Its use was discontinued at circa serial #1,360,000 by Springfield and at circa serial #1,300,000 by Winchester.

The **Type 3** front sight screw lacked the rebated head. Its full diameter was 0.361 inch. Two types of this screw were used, one with a knurled and the other with a smooth head. Both were used at the same time to the end of production.

The M1 Garand

NOTE: Many front sight screws have been observed marked "A" at the bottom of the socket. The "A" stood for Allen Screw Company, the originator and manufacturer of the socket head screw. It was not a Winchester inspection marking and so will be equally correct on Springfield or Winchester M1 Garands.

Front Sight Screw Seal

The front sight seal (drawing number A152855) was a cup-shaped piece of steel press-fitted into the front sight screw hole to prevent

the troops from making unauthorized changes in the position of the front sight. It was punched from a disk of thin steel and was 0.385 inch in diameter. The seal was blued originally. See Figure 66.

Figure 66   Once in place, a hole had to be drilled into the seal so that an Allen wrench could be inserted though the seal to back out the screw. Its use was discontinued in late February 1943 at circa serial #1,360,000 by Springfield and circa serial #1,300,000 by Winchester a few months later.

STACKING SWIVEL ASSEMBLY

The stacking swivel assembly consisted of the stacking swivel and the stacking swivel screw. The same assembly was used during the entire production of the M1 Garand. There is no reliable way to discern the differences between manufacturers. See Figure 67.

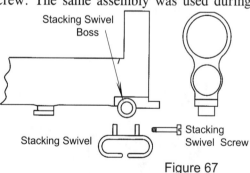

Stacking Swivel Boss

Stacking Swivel

Stacking Swivel Screw

Figure 67

Stacking Swivel

The stacking swivel was manufactured from sheet steel 0.170 inch in diameter and formed into a "C"

The M1 Garand

shape 0.620 inch wide by 1.466 inches long. The opening in the "C" was 0.240 inch.

The two hinge brackets on the back of the stacking swivel fit on either side of the stacking swivel boss on the gas cylinder. They were 0.345 inch wide at the widest point and 0.15 inch thick. They were drilled with a 0.18-inch-diameter hole to accept the stacking swivel screw. The right swivel bracket had a smooth interior and the left swivel bracket was threaded. The swivel was Parkerized.

Stacking swivels used on early gas trap M1 Garand rifles to circa serial #20,000 were marked with the drawing number B8891.

NOTE: The stacking swivel and screw are often replaced on recent reimported M1 Garands with parts not as well made or symmetrical as those of original American manufacture. They can often be distinguished by a light gray or black oxide color.

Stacking Swivel Screw
The stacking swivel screw was 0.8 inch long. It had a slotted fillister head 0.260 inch in diameter by 0.09 inch high. The screw shank was 0.18 inch in diameter by 0.7 inch long. The screw was Parkerized. Stacking swivel screw tips were upset to prevent the screw from backing out and becoming lost. The gas cylinder manufacturer can sometimes be determined by the way the screw is upset. Figure 67A shows the most common stacking swivel screws the authors have identified. During the long production period, Springfield will vary from a concave to a flat stake. Other types are often from replaced screws.

| Springfield | Winchester | Harrington & Richardson | International Harvester |

Figure 67A

The M1 Garand

STOCKS

Nearly six million M1 Garand stocks (drawing number D35467) were manufactured for new rifles, and unknown millions more were made for use as replacement stocks. The vast majority of original M1 Garand stocks were made of straight-grained American black walnut with a linseed oil finish. In the mid-1950s, birch was made as a substitute for walnut. Harrington & Richardson supplied birch stocks with many of their later M1s, and many more were used as replacement stocks.

The M1 Garand stock measured 29.75 inches long overall. It was 5.0 inches high at the butt (1), 1.75 inches high at the trigger guard plate well (2) and 1.35 inches high at the front, just behind the stock ferrule lip (3). It was 1.95 inches wide at the butt (4), 2.0 inches wide just above the trigger (5), and 1.60 inches wide at the front, just behind the stock ferrule lip (6). See Figure 68.

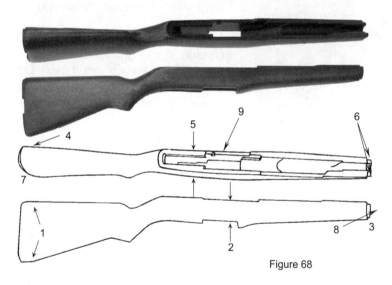

Figure 68

The buttstock was inletted 0.05 inch wide by 0.2 inch deep around the circumference (7) to allow the butt plate to cap the end. The butt also had two butt plate screw holes. The top hole was 1.2 inches below the inletted lip and the bottom screw hole was 1 inch above the inletted lip.

The M1 Garand

The front of the stock was shaped into a lip 0.135 inch long by 0.33 inch thick at the thickest point and 0.19 inch thick at the thinnest point (8). The stock lip fitted into the stock ferrule and was held in place by friction when the stock was removed from the receiver/barrel assembly and by the forward band when assembled.

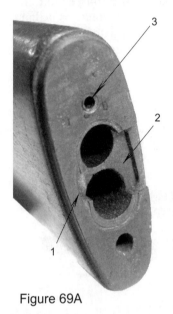

Figure 69A

After circa serial #70,000 for Springfield-made M1s and circa serial #1,240,000 for Winchester-made M1s, the area around the two holes was inletted for the butt plate trap door hinge and catch. See Figure 69A. The wood was cut away in a 0.5-inch-diameter semicircle to the left (1) and a 1.2-inch-wide slot or notch to the right (2). A lip 0.12 inch deep was left to edge the slot (3).

In spite of the huge numbers of M1 Garand stocks manufactured, there were only four distinct types—and a provisional fifth—which are described in the following paragraphs and tables.

Type 1 M1 Garand Stocks

All Type 1 M1 Garand stocks used the solid butt plate and had a long (approximately 2.150-inch) barrel channel neck.

There were three variations of the **Type 1** stock: Springfield only made the **Type 1A** stocks to circa serial #30,000. The drawing number was stamped behind the pistol grip and it did not have a provision for the cleaning kit and tools in the buttstock. The two holes that were drilled into the stock were done to lighten it. The top hole was 1 inch in diameter and the bottom hole 0.56 inch in diameter.

Type 1B M1 Garand stocks did not show the drawing number; otherwise, they were identical to the Type 1A. Both Springfield

The M1 Garand

(circa serial #s 30,001-50,000) and Winchester (circa serial #s 100,001-1,240,000) manufactured the Type 1B stock.

Type 1C M1 Garand stocks were similar to the Type 1B except for the top and bottom lightening holes which were changed to 0.81 inch in diameter. The Type 1C was used by Springfield only from circa serial #s 50,001 to 70,000.

TYPE 2 M1 GARAND STOCKS
Four variations of the Type 2 M1 Garand stocks were produced.

Type 2A M1 Garand stocks were used by Springfield from circa serial #s 70,001-480,000 (early 1942). The lightening holes were 0.81 inch in diameter, the barrel channel neck was 2.15 inches long (see Figure 69B) and it was the first M1 stock variation to be inletted to accept the Type 2 butt plate cap plate.

Winchester changed to the **Type 2A** stock at circa serial #s 1,240,001 to 2,300,000 (late 1943).

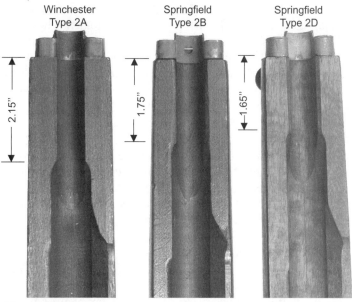

Figure 69B

The M1 Garand

Type 2B M1 Garand stocks were in use by Springfield from circa serial #s 480,001-950,000 and by Winchester from circa serial #2,300,001 to the end of their production. The barrel channel neck was shortened to 1.75 inches (refer to Figure 69B).

Type 2C M1 Garand stocks were used by Springfield from circa serial #950,001 to the end of production; by International Harvester for all production and by Harrington & Richardson—although mixed with Type 3 stocks toward the end of production. This stock was the same as the Type 2B except that the relief cut for the clip latch on the left side was cut straight down instead of at an inward angle. Refer to arrow 9 in Figure 68.

Type 2D M1 Garand stocks were replacement stocks apparently made at the end of, or after World War II. They were made of a poorer grade of walnut and can be identified by the slightly shorter barrel channel neck which was 1.65 inches long. The edges of the channel were relieved with a slanting cut. Refer to Figure 69B.

TYPE 3 M1 GARAND STOCK
From the mid-1950s on, the **Type 3** birch stock was the substitute standard for M1 Garand replacement stocks. They were identical to Type 2C walnut stocks except that the barrel channel neck was 1.75 inches long. The birch stock was intended as a replacement stock but many H & RA and some very late-production Springfield M1 Garands were originally furnished with birch stocks. They will show all the proper inspection markings.

TYPE 4 M1 GARAND STOCK
The **Type 4** stock was identical to the Type 2C but modified for Type 3 National Match M1 Garands with fiberglass panels inletted into the receiver area. These stocks were finished with "China," or "tung" oil, a type of varnish, to seal the wood against moisture. See Appendix C for a further discussion.

TYPE 5 M1 GARAND STOCK
A **Type 5** stock blank has been observed recently. It appears to have been made by laminating two walnut blanks together, possibly blanks that were undersized or rejected for blemishes. The

The M1 Garand

samples observed had S.A./J.L.G. cartouches. Look for differing grain patterns and a glue line where the two pieces of wood were joined. The Type 5 stocks are thought to have been made only during the Korean War period when sufficient gunstock-quality walnut was becoming very scarce. To date, no records have been found to positively identify this type.

NOTE: Other woods, principally Asian mahogany and European beech, have been used by foreign militaries to manufacture stocks for M1 Garands they acquired as military aid. Only American black walnut or birch (on Harrington & Richardson and late-Springfield-made M1 Garands) can be considered U.S. military-issue original stocks.

WINCHESTER STOCKS—NOTES

Winchester stocks were **Type 1B** from circa serial #100,001-1,240,000. The **Type 2A** stocks were in use from circa serial #1,240,001 to 2,300,000. The **Type 2B** stock followed in use from circa serial #2,300,001 to the end of production, including the Win-13 series (1,600,000-1,640,000). Those Winchester stocks which have had their cartouche removed during refurbishing may be identified by the fact that the pistol grip arches

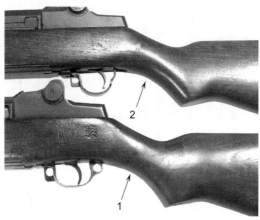

Figure 70A

higher and curves downward over and ahead of the trigger area, see Figure 70A (arrows 1 and 2). Also, the end of the groove in-letted for the trigger guard forms a wide "V" behind the trigger guard, rather than a "U"-shaped channel as do the Springfield, International Harvester or Harrington & Richardson M1 stocks, see Figure 70B.

125

The M1 Garand

Table 23
M1 Garand Stock Type Identification Guide (inches)
(All stocks are American Black Walnut unless otherwise noted)

Type	Serial # Range	Drawing # Marked	Buttstock Hole Size	Butt Plate	Barrel Channel Neck	Clip Latch Relief Angle
Springfield						
1A	81-30,000	Behind Pistol Grip	1.0/0.56	Solid	2.150	Inward Angle
1B	30,001-50,000	None	1.0/0.56	Solid	2.150	Inward Angle
1C	50,001-70,000	None	0.81/0.81	Solid	2.150	Inward Angle
2A	70,001-480,000	None	0.81/0.81	Butt plate cap (1)	2.150	Inward Angle
2B	480,001-950,000	None	0.81/0.81	Butt plate cap	1.750	Inward Angle
2C	950,001 to end of production	None	0.81/0.81	Butt plate cap	1.750	Straight
2D	End of, or post-World War II production	None	0.81/0.81	Butt plate cap	1.650	Straight
3	Substitute Standard from mid-1950s (2) Birch	None	0.81/0.81	Butt plate cap	1.750	Straight
4	National Match (3)	None	0.81/0.81	Butt plate cap	1.750	Straight

Table 23, cont.
M1 Garand Stock Type Identification Guide (inches)
(All stocks are American Black Walnut unless otherwise noted)

Type	Serial # Range	Drawing # Marked	Buttstock Hole Size	Butt Plate	Barrel Channel Neck	Clip Latch Relief Angle
5	Laminated Walnut (4)	None	0.81/0.81	Butt plate cap	1.650	Straight
Winchester						
1B	100,001-1,240,000	None	1.0/0.56	Solid	2.150	Straight
2A	1,240,001-2,300,000	None	0.81/0.81	Butt plate cap (1)	2.150	Straight
2B	2,300,001 to end of production, including 1,600,000-1,640,000	None	0.81/0.81	Butt plate cap	1.750	Straight
International Harvester						
2C	All production	None	0.81/0.81	Butt plate cap	1.750	Straight
Harrington & Richardson						
2C	All production	None	0.81/0.81	Butt plate cap	1.750	Straight
3	Late production (2)	None	0.81/0.81	Butt plate cap	1.750	Straight

1   Stock inletted for butt plate with butt plate cap for access to cleaning equipment
2   Shortage of suitable walnut led to the adoption of birch as a substitute standard
3   Fiberglass panels were inletted into receiver area of National Match stocks starting in 1960
4   Provisional type only. Two walnut blanks glued together to produce large-enough blank for stock. Small number observed with S.A./J.L.G. cartouche

The M1 Garand

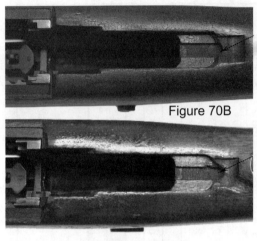

Figure 70B

Top, Springfield; bottom, Winchester

Winchester changed the lightening hole diameter in the buttstock from 1 inch over 0.56 inch in diameter to both holes at 0.81 inch in diameter at circa serial #1,240,001.

Winchester stocks also have an 0.875-inch-long by 0.2-inch-wide and 0.15-inch-deep indent in the stock below the right rear side of the receiver, see Figure 70C (arrow).

International Harvester M1 Garand Stocks—Notes

Early stocks made by International Harvester, see Figure 71, are marked in the barrel channel with one or two letters (arrow 1) and a four-digit number (arrow 2). Later stocks show only the four-digit number. The numbers are 0.220 inch high. The stamps were made convex to allow the number to be stamped into the rounded barrel channel. International Harvester stocks are

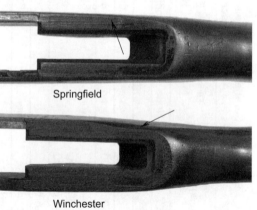

Springfield

Winchester

Figure 70C

indented on the right side behind the operating rod slot like the Winchester stocks (arrow 3). International Harvester stocks can also often be identified by sighting along the left side from the buttstock forward and noting the uneven milling marks.

The M1 Garand

HARRINGTON & RICHARDSON M1 GARAND STOCKS—NOTES

The apron of stocks made by Harrington & Richardson is noticeably thicker, especially on the right side, when compared to other M1 Garand stocks, see Figure 72 (arrow). Later-production H&R rifles were built with Type 3 birch stocks and either walnut or birch handguards. Harrington & Richardson used the small (0.375-inch-square) Defense Acceptance stamp on their early M1

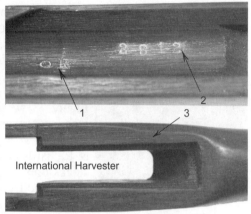

International Harvester

Figure 71

Garand stocks but changed to the large (0.5-inch-square) Defense Acceptance stamp for the later production.

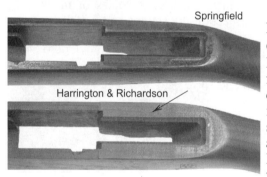

Springfield

Harrington & Richardson

Figure 72

Inspection Cartouche

Every M1 Garand rifle was given a thorough quality control inspection under the supervision of an authorized Ordnance Department officer who accepted the rifles. He, or his staff, examined each rifle according to written set of procedures. If the rifle passed this final examination, it was stamped with the initials of the manufacturer and the authorized officer or the commanding officer of Springfield Armory in a cartouche. This cartouche, or wood stamp, was generally square in shape with rounded corners and contained the manufacturer's and officer's initials to September-October 1953. The

The M1 Garand

various inspection stamps used throughout the production of the M1 Garand are shown in Tables 23A and B, Table 24, and Table 25.

After September-October 1953, the Defense Department acceptance stamp was substituted. It consisted of the federal eagle below three stars, all contained in a box with rounded corners. It was stamped on the left side of the stock above the trigger. This new cartouche (see Figure 73) was used in two sizes: 0.5 inch square and 0.375 inch square. The latter size was used by Harrington & Richardson on its early M1 Garand stocks only. Do not confuse this version of the Department of Defense acceptance cartouche with a similar cartouche consisting of the three stars and

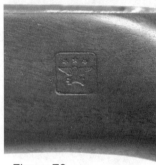

Figure 73

eagle within a circle that was used to mark other federal property, but never firearms.

WARNING: In recent years, counterfeit copies of many U.S. Ordnance Department inspection die stamps and cartouches have been made available, ostensibly for the purpose of renewing those markings removed or obscured during repair and refurbishment programs. In many cases, these die stamps and cartouches have been used on unmarked replacement stocks to make a potential buyer think he or she was buying an original rifle. One in particular should be noted here, see Figure 74. It was obtained from a large company that specializes in gun parts and was a copy of the Defense Department federal eagle and stars acceptance

Figure 74

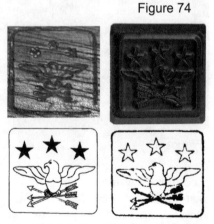

Clockwise from top, right: Original Defense Department inspection cartouche; counterfeit die stamp; drawing used in Figure 73, 1st-3rd editions; inking from counterfeit die stamp.

The M1 Garand

stamp. The die was apparently photo etched from the drawing made by the author and used as Figure 73 in the previous three editions of this book. The drawing was done freehand for illustrative purposes and only generally represented the original die stamp. It is reproduced here in Figure 74 with a photograph of and an inking from the counterfeit die. If you see this particular die marking on an M1 Garand or M14 stock you can be assured that it is not an original stock.

Ordnance Department Cartouche

Beginning at circa serial #80,000, the Ordnance Department required the application of their "Crossed Cannon" cartouche to M1 stocks. Two sizes of the cartouche were used. The first was 0.72 inch in diameter (muzzle to breech) and was used from circa serial #s 80,000-410,000 to 525,000. The second and smaller size was 0.44 inch in diameter (muzzle to breech) and it was used from circa serial #s 410,001-525,001 to 4,275,000. See Figure 75.

Figure 75

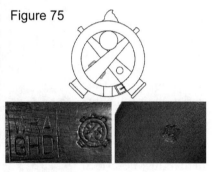

From circa serial #s 1,800,000 to 3,890,000, many original M1 Garand stocks will show the small Ordnance Department Crossed Cannon cartouche stamped into the heel of the pistol grip, refer to Figure 75.

NOTE 1: From late 1941 to mid-1942 (circa serial #s 410,000-525,000), both the large- and small-diameter "Crossed Cannon" cartouches were in use at the same time on S.A./G.H.S. stocks. A few examples of the large-diameter crossed cannon have been observed on later S.A./E.Mc.F. and S.A./G.A.W. cartouched stocks, but they are rare.

NOTE 2: After World War II, M1 Garands that had served in battle or had been damaged underwent a complete rebuilding. All serviceable parts—including stocks—were reused and the rifles were rebuilt, refinished, test-fired and inspected following the

The M1 Garand

same criteria as a newly built M1 Garand. After completion, they were marked on the stock with a cartouche as described in Table 23B. However, the Ordnance Department cartouche was generally removed during the stock-refinishing process which included scraping and sanding. Only those M1 Garands that passed through the "Clean and Repair" program at Springfield Armory were re-marked with the inspection cartouches, S.A./S.H.M. and S.A./J.L.G., and the Ordnance Department "P" firing proof (0.44 inch in diameter) and the crossed cannons marking. Occasionally, the original cartouches and proof marks remained visible.

Proof Firing Cartouche

The "P" proof indicating test firing was stamped on the forward portion of the pistol grip. Five variations of the firing proof mark were used, see Figure 76 for the various types of markings described in the following paragraphs.

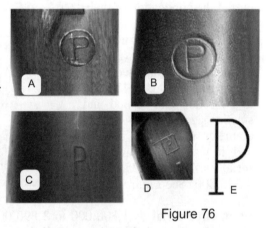

Figure 76

The original marking on all Springfield- and Winchester-manufactured Garand stocks was the letter "P" with serifs in a circle (A). The letter was 0.320 ± 0.01 inch high and its circle was 0.520 ± 0.02 inch in diameter from start to end of production.

H&R stocks showed the circled "P" with serifs to circa serial #4,600,000 and the sans serif circled "P" thereafter (B).

IHC used the circled "P" without serifs (B) to circa serial #4,800,000 in conjunction with the Ordnance Department's crossed cannon acceptance stamp for their first few thousand M1s. The large Defense Acceptance stamp (0.5 inch) was used thereafter to the end of their production.

The M1 Garand

NOTE: Markings stamped into wood will vary slightly in size depending on how hard they were struck, the density of the wood, and the amount of wear incurred across the marking. As a rule of thumb, markings struck deeply will be larger.

The "P" without serifs (C) found on walnut or birch replacement stocks—other than those made at Springfield—was not contained with a circle. It was used by the facilities at Anniston Army Depot, Augusta Arsenal, Raritan Arsenal and the Red River Arsenal, later Red River Army Depot.

The rebuild facilities at San Antonio Arsenal (and for a short time, Red River Arsenal) used a "P" without serifs stamped within a 0.37-inch-wide square box (D).

Benicia Arsenal stamped a "P" with curled serifs inside a circle, but they placed it on the bottom of the pistol grip (E).

Table 25 presents a list of rebuild facilities and the style of firing proof they marked on rifles passing through their hands. Note serifs or lack of serifs on the "P" mark. The M1 Garand rebuilding program began at Springfield Armory in the fall of 1945 and was officially known as the "Clean and Repair" program.

Clean and Repair Program

By the end of World War II, millions of M1 Garands were badly in need of overhaul. At Springfield Armory, a major "Clean and Repair" program was started. In addition to the Springfield "Clean and Repair" program, many other M1 Garands underwent repair at Army maintenance facilities around the world from the end of World War II well into the late 1960s. Do not confuse the "Clean and Repair" program with minor repair work performed below arsenal level, or with continuing work carried out at Springfield and other arsenals which might be termed product improvements and resulted in the M1C, M1D and MC52 sniper rifles as well as the National Match M1 Rifles, see Appendices B and C. M1 Garands that went through the "Clean and Repair" program were usually marked on the stock with the initials of the arsenal or depot performing the work. Sometimes initials of the inspector were seen as well, in a cartouche that replaced or, more rarely, was stamped in addition to the manufacturing arsenal's inspection cartouche (see below). M1 Garands undergoing "clean and repair" were test-fired and so marked with the "P" proof. These markings are described in Table 25. Collectors today generally refer to an M1 Garand that passed through the "Clean and Repair" program as "rebuilt."

Table 23A
Army Inspector of Ordnance
Cartouches

S.A. S.P.G.	S.A. G.H.S.	S.A. E.McF.
81 - 78,000	78,001 - 700,000	700,001 - 1,860,000
S.A. G.A.W.	S.A. N.F.R.	S.A. S.H.M.
1,860,001 - 3,200,000	3,200,001-3,890,000	Any prior serial number under 3,890,000
S.A. J.L.G.	S.A. R.	W.R.A. R.S.
4,200,000 - 4,320,000 to 4,350,000	Any serial number (rebuild)	100,001-120,000
W.R.A. W.B.	W.R.A. W.B.	W.R.A. G.H.D.
120,001 - 130,000	130,001 - 1,220,000	1,220,001 - 2,655,982 and 1,600,000 - 1,640,000

Note: See Table 24 for conditions of use.

The M1 Garand

Table 23B
Army Inspector of Ordnance Cartouches—Rebuild

S.A. B	S.A. W.	BA JLC
Post 1948 (rebuild)	Other observed letters are C, F, H, O, R, S, and T	Benicia Arsenal (rebuild)

HOD WB	RIA EB	OG
Hawaii Ordnance Depot	Rock Island Arsenal	Ogden Arsenal

AN	AAS	MR
Anniston Arsenal	Augusta Arsenal	Mount Rainer Arsenal

O.G.E.K.	OGEK	O.G.
Ogden Arsenal	Ogden Arsenal	Ogden Arsenal

O.G.	OG	RA
Ogden Arsenal	Ogden Arsenal	Raritan Arsenal

RA-P		R.R.A.
Raritan Arsenal		Red River Arsenal

RRAD	C S.A.A.	C-S.A.A.
Red River Army Depot	San Antonio Arsenal (left side)	San Antonio Arsenal (Right Side)

SAA-1	H-S.A.A.	L-SAA
San Antonio Arsenal	San Antonio Arsenal	San Antonio Arsenal

The M1 Garand

Table 24			
M1 Garand Stock Marking Identification Guide			
Springfield National Armory Production, Pre- and World War II			
Barrel Date	**Stock Cartouche (1,2)**	**Size inches (6)**	**Serial Number Range**
1936 - 1940	S.A./S.P.G.	0.72 x 0.85	81-78,000 approx.
9/40 - 6/1942	S.A./G.H.S.	0.72 x 0.79	78,001-700,000
6/1942 - 7/1943	S.A./E.McF. (5)	0.72 x 0.83	700,001-1,860,000
7/1943 - 10/1944	S.A./G.A.W. (5)	0.72 x 0.83	1,860,001-3,200,000
10/1944 - 11/1945	S.A./N.F.R. (5)	0.72 x 0.83	3,200,001-3,890,000
Reconditioning Period (WW II and 1946-1948) (1) (2)			
11/45 - 12/47	S.A./S.H.M.	0.72 x 0.83	Any prior serial number including Winchester
8/47-5/50	S.A./R.A. S.A./H. (open box)	0.72 x 0.85	Any prior serial number including Winchester (questionable)
Korean War and Later Springfield Production			
7/50 - 9-10/53	S.A./J.L.G.	0.72 x 0.82	4,200,000-4,320,000 to 4,350,000
9-10/53-end of production	Defense Eagle (3)	0.5 x 0.5	4,320,000-4,350,000 to end of production
Arsenal Rebuilding Identification			
Any barrel date	S.A./C or F, H,O,R,S,T and W	0.9 x 0.9	Any serial number
Winchester Production			
Undated (4)	W.R.A./R.S.	1.0 x 1.0	100,001 - 120,000
Undated (4)	W.R.A./W.B. (W.B. boxed)	1.0 x 1.0	120,001 - 130,000
Undated (4)	W.R.A./W.B. (W.B. unboxed)	1.0 x 1.0	130,001 - 1,220,000

Table 24, cont. M1 Garand Stock Marking Identification Guide			
Barrel Date	Stock Cartouche (1, 2)	Size Inches (6)	Serial Number Range
Undated (4)	W.R.A./G.H.D.	0.8 x 0.8	1,220,001 - 2,655,982 (including Win-13)
International Harvester Production			
LMR 1953-1956	Cross Cannon Defense Eagle	0.72 dia. 0.5 x 0.5	4,400,000-4,404,000 4,404,001 - EOP
Harrington & Richardson Production			
HRA 1953 - 1956	Defense Eagle	0.375 x 0.375 & 0.5 x 0.5	4,400,000 - 5,600,000 5,600,001 - end of production

1 Cartouches are shown in Tables 23A and B.
2 As World War II was coming to a close, thousands of M1 Garands were rebuilt and refurbished to eliminate battle damage. These will show a mix of parts but are desirable to collectors because they are true battle rifles. They will usually show the initials of the arsenal doing the rebuilding stamped in the stock. Those stocks replaced by "Post Armorers" will not show any markings.
3 Beginning in September-October 1953, the Defense Eagle Acceptance stamp replaced the cartouche containing the initials of the Springfield Armory and its commanding officer.
4 Winchester barrels were undated but can be identified by the part number—WRA D35448—stamped in script form on top of the barrel under the rear handguard. The only dated Winchester barrels were made in the 1960s as replacement barrels.
5 The Ordnance Department acceptance stamps (crossed cannons), 0.131 inch in diameter from breech to bore, will be found on the bottom of the M1 Garand pistol grip on stocks late in the E.McF. series and all through the G.A.W. and into the early N.F.R. series. It will often be found on arsenal-rebuilt stocks as well.
6 Sizes will vary 0.01-0.02 inch due to density of wood, depth of strike and wear.
7 Stanley P. Gibbs assisted in proofing M1 rifles undergoing rebuild during this period.

After September-October 1953, when the Department of Defense Acceptance Stamp replaced the cartouches containing Arsenal and inspector initials for new-production M1 Garands (and National Match rifles), Springfield continued to use the box-style cartouche for rifles undergoing "clean and repair." Two styles of cartouches are apparent: Type 1 Clean and Repair cartouches are open on the

The M1 Garand

bottom while Type 2 Clean and Repair cartouches are closed. The Type 1 Clean and Repair cartouches may or may not have an inspector's initial beneath the "S.A." Type 2 Clean and Repair cartouches always contain an inspector's initial, beneath the "S.A." Inspector's initials observed to date include C, F, H, O, R, S, T and W.

Table 25			
"Clean & Repair" Program Stock Markings			
Clean and Repair Facility	**Left Side of Stock**	**Right Side**	**Firing Proof**
Anniston Army Depot	AN		P (no serifs)
Augusta Arsenal	AAG (pre-1960)	AA1204 (post-1960)	P (no serifs)
Benicia Arsenal	BA/JPL (boxed)		Circled P with serifs, bottom of grip
	BA/CAB (boxed)		Circled P with serifs, bottom of grip
	BA-WT (boxed)		
Hawaii Ordnance Depot	HOD/WB (may show under receiver)		Circled P
	HOD/WB		Circled P
Mount Rainier Ordnance Depot	MR		Circled P
Ogden Arsenal	O.G.E.K. (Elmer Keith) (boxed)		Circled P
	OGEK (Edward Klouser) (no box)		Circled P
	O.G.		May have a Circled P
	OG or OG (boxed)		May have a Circled P
Raritan Arsenal	RA		P (no serifs)
	RA-P		No P

The M1 Garand

Clean and Repair Facility	Left Side of Stock	Right Side	Firing Proof
Table 25, cont. "Clean & Repair" Program Stock Markings			
Red River Arsenal (Prior to 1945)	R.R.A. (1) or	R.R.A. (2)	Circled P (no serifs)
Red River Arsenal (1945 and later)	R.R.A. (1) or	R.R.A. (2)	Boxed P (no serifs)
Red River Army Depot	RRAD (1) or	RRAD (2)	Boxed P (no serifs)
Rock Island Arsenal	RIA/EB (1) (boxed)		Circled P (serifs, bottom of grip)
San Antonio Arsenal	C S.A.A. (boxed) or	C-S.A.A. (boxed)	Circled P
	SAA-1		Boxed P
	H-S.A.A.		Boxed P
	L-SAA		Boxed P
Springfield Armory (3)	S.A./S.H.M. (boxed)		Circled P serifs
	S.A./(various single initials)		Circled P serifs
New Rifles Only	S.A./J.L.G. (4) (boxed)		Circled P serifs
	S.A./J.L.G (5) (boxed)		Circled P serifs
	S.A./R.A. (open box) (5)		Circled P serifs
	S.A./R (open box) (5)		Circled P serifs
	Defense Department Acceptance Stamp		Circled P serifs

Table 25, cont.			
"Clean & Repair" Program Stock Markings			
Clean and Repair Facility	**Left Side of Stock**	**Right Side**	**Firing Proof**
1 Marked on left side of buttstock, rather than on stock above the trigger. 2 Marked on right side of buttstock, rather than above the trigger. 3 All Springfield Cartouches are contained in boxes with rounded corners. 4 Cartouche was 0.72 x 0.82 inch. 5 The Ordnance Department Cartouche was reapplied on M1 Garands with these inspector markings (boxed).			

STOCK FERRULE

The stock ferrule assembly consisted of three pieces: 1) ferrule, 2) forward sling swivel, and 3) slotted sling swivel screw. See Figure 77.

Figure 77

The stock ferrule proper, drawing number C40613, fitted over a lip on the forward end of the stock. It was 1.520 inches wide by 1.490 inches high and 0.40 inch thick, front to back. A U-shaped channel was formed from the sheet metal of the facing plate that was 0.610 inch wide by 0.675 inch long. The reverse of the stock

The M1 Garand

ferrule was hollow to accommodate the stock lip. The bottom of the stock ferrule was divided into two eyes to hold the stock ferrule swivel and screw. The left eye was threaded 10-32NF. Two types of stock ferrules were made.

Type 1 stock ferrules were forged and milled at the Springfield Armory and used to circa serial #90,000. Two variations were produced. **Variation 1** had the drawing number stamped on the front face and was used to circa serial #13,000. **Variation 2** did not and was in use to circa serial #90,000. The Type 1 stock ferrule can be identified by its sharper corners and one-piece construction. Metal thickness was 0.075 inch at the bottom of the "U"-shaped channel and 0.064 inch at the sides. Expect some variation due to the machining process.

Type 2 stock ferrules were stamped from sheet steel 0.065 inch thick in two pieces and brazed together after circa serial #90,000. Three variations of the Type 2 stock ferrule have been identified. **Variation 1** did not have a hole at the bottom of the U-shaped channel. These were in use from circa serial #s 90,000-400,000. **Variation 2** had a hole 0.12 inch in diameter and was in use from circa serial #s 400,001-510,000. **Variation 3** had a hole 0.190 inch in diameter and was in use from circa serial #s 510,001 to the end of production. All Type 2 stock ferrules were 0.050 inch thick at the bottom of the "U"-shaped channel and 0.0550 inch thick at the sides. Type 2 stock ferrules are identified by their thinner metal and the four tabs visible on the side of the upper front face.

Winchester manufactured **Type 1** stock ferrules to circa serial #1,200,000; after, they manufactured the **Type 2** in two variations. **Variation 1** had the 0.12-inch-diameter hole at the bottom of the barrel channel. The **Variation 2** which was used to the end of production had the 0.190-inch-diameter hole. It is not known when exactly the change took place.

Some Winchester Type 2 stock ferrules are marked with the letter "T" and may also show a number. The marking is found on the inside of the ferrule. In some cases, the hole is visibly off center to the left or right.

The M1 Garand

All International Harvester and Harrington & Richardson stock ferrules were the Type 2, 3rd variation with the large, 0.190-inch-diameter hole.

Stock Ferrule Swivel

The stock ferrule swivel (drawing number B8890) or forward sling swivel, as it is sometimes referred to, was 1.75 inches wide by 0.710 inch high. It was stamped to shape and the diameter of the swivel was 0.185 inch. The swivel had a single disk-shaped post centered on the top bar of the swivel 0.175 inch wide by 0.40 inch high by 0.345 inch in diameter. It was drilled 0.2 inch in diameter to accept the stock ferrule swivel screw. All stock ferrule swivels were Parkerized and usually cannot be differentiated between manufacturers. The same swivel was also used on the Springfield 1903A1 rifle and the M1 and M2 .22-Caliber training rifles. Early examples to circa serial #50,000 were marked with the drawing number. No physical changes were made to the stock ferrule swivel during M1 Garand production.

Stock Ferrule Swivel Screw

The stock ferrule swivel screw was 0.185 inch in diameter and 0.610 inch long. It had a slotted fillister head 0.260 inch in diameter and 0.30 inch high. The lower 0.150 inch of the shank was threaded 10-32NF. No changes were made to the stock ferrule swivel screw during M1 Garand production. Early gas trap screws were blued; all others were Parkerized.

NOTE 1: The stock ferrule swivel screw was staked after installation to prevent its working loose in the field. Do not try to turn the screw all the way out or you may damage the threads.

NOTE 2: Recently, reproductions of stock cartouche dies have appeared on the market. They were intended to be used to "refresh" existing cartouches that have been obscured or removed by rough usage while in the service or during refurbishment. Some unscrupulous individuals have used them to apply stock inspection cartouches to replacement and newly made stocks. One die encountered by the authors was "S.A./E.McF." The original cartouche was 0.72 by 0.83 inch square but the counterfeit die was 0.85 by 0.91 inches and rectangular. Be careful.

The M1 Garand

BUTT PLATE ASSEMBLY

Two major types of butt plates were produced for the M1 Garand. The **Type 1** was designed for the early M1 Garand stocks without the two holes in the buttstock which were used to lighten the weight and store the cleaning and tool kit. This butt plate (drawing number C41012) can be identified by its lack of butt plate cap and by its distinct reinforcing rings around the upper and lower screw holes. It had 16 diamonds in the horizontal row immediately below the upper screw hole. The upper screw hole was 1.175 inches below the top and the lower was centered 1.90 inches above the bottom of the butt plate. The screw holes were 0.20 to 0.25 inch in diameter and countersunk 0.250 to 0.310 inch. The earliest butt plates have the drawing number stamped inside. The Type 1 butt plate was used by Springfield from the start of production to circa serial #70,000 and by Winchester to circa serial #160,000. See Figure 78A.

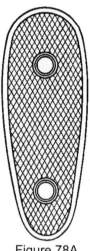

Figure 78A

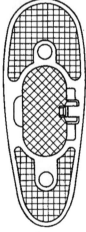

Figure 78B

The **Type 2** butt plate (drawing number C64283) was used on the M1 Garand stock from circa serial #70,000 to the end of production. The butt plate was 4.980 inches high by 1.870 inches wide at its widest point and stamped from sheet metal 0.80 inch thick. It had two screw holes; the upper was centered 1.175 inches below the top and the lower centered 1.90 inches above the bottom of the butt plate. The screw holes were 0.20 to 0.25 inch in diameter and countersunk 0.250 to 0.310 inch. The butt plate cap cutout was centered 2.490 inches below the top and was 0.94 inch wide by 1.93 inches high. The exterior area was recessed to allow the cap to fit flush when closed. See Figure 78B.

The butt plate cap was a casting machined to size. It was 2.10 inches high by 1.30 inches wide. A hinge piece with two ears and a semitubular enclosure was cast into the cap. The cap was attached to the butt plate with a steel pin 0.025 inch in diameter by 1.0 inch long. A spring and plunger was inserted into the tubular enclosure to supply tension to keep the cap closed. The plunger was 0.80 inch long and made in two variations; the first had a rounded end and was used by Springfield throughout World War II production. Winchester used the second-variation rounded plunger until the "Win-13" production (circa serial #s 1,600,000-1,640,000). Scott Duff reported in a personal communication to the authors that postwar plungers appear to be of the second, rounded type. The catch portion was 0.138 inch in diameter. No changes were made to the Type 2 butt plate or the cap plunger mechanism to the end of production of the M1 Garand. See Figure 79.

It is possible to differentiate between butt plates made for the M1 Garand by the four manufacturers primarily by the checkering pattern applied, and by the butt plate screw hole countersink. The differences are explained in Table 26. Winchester was the only manufacturer to produce a marked butt plate.

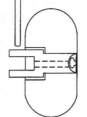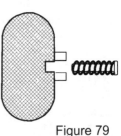

Figure 79

NOTE: Butt plates made by Pietro Beretta for the Italian M59 rifle have an indented checkered pattern while those made for the American M1 Garand rifle have raised checkering.

BUTT SWIVEL

The butt swivel (drawing number B8889) made the transition from gas trap rifle to gas port rifle and continued to the end of M14 (!) production without a major change. Very early butt swivels for the gas port rifle were marked "B-8889" or "B 8889" but this practice was discontinued at circa serial #40,000 and they remained unmarked by all manufacturers from that point on. See Figure 80.

The butt swivel was 1.70 inches wide and the diameter of the swivel varied from 0.165 to 0.170 inch. Formed at the same time

The M1 Garand

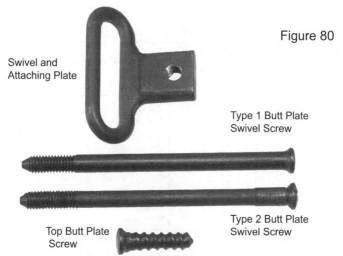

Figure 80

Swivel and
Attaching Plate

Type 1 Butt Plate
Swivel Screw

Type 2 Butt Plate
Swivel Screw

Top Butt Plate
Screw

was the attaching plate which was 0.65 inch wide by 0.70 inch high and 0.235 inch thick. It was drilled and tapped 12-28 for the butt plate/sling swivel screw. The butt swivel was Parkerized. Except for a more definite separation between the swivel and its post, the usual punch mark and slightly rougher finish of the Winchester-made butt swivels, there is no reliable way to identify them by manufacturer.

Butt Swivel Screw

The buttstock swivel screw served to attach both the butt plate and the swivel plate to the stock. It was a slotted flat-head screw 3.245 inches long overall with a head diameter of 0.30 inch, refer to Figure 80. Two types of butt swivel screws were used. The **Type 1** screw had a constant diameter of 0.390 inch and was marked with the part number to circa serial #5,000. The **Type 2** screw was also 0.390 inch in diameter below the head but only for 0.210 inch, at which point the shaft diameter narrowed to 0.190 inch. The screw had a 12-28 machine screw thread 0.690 inch long. The tip was a flat point. It passed through the butt plate and buttstock and screwed into the threaded plate on the buttstock swivel. It is not known when the Type 2 screw superseded the Type 1. No other changes were made to the buttstock swivel screw during the production of the M1 Garand. There is no way to identify them by manufacturer.

The M1 Garand

Table 26		
Butt Plate Identification Guide		
Manufacturer/ Type	**Serial Number Range**	**Identifying Characteristics**
Solid Butt Plate		
Springfield (C41012) Type 1	1-70,000	No cap, narrow border around checkering, distinct reinforcing rings around upper and lower screw holes, 16 diamonds in horizontal row immediately below the upper screw hole, 5.5 checks across top row, drawing number stamped on the inside in earliest butt plates
Winchester Type 1	100,001-160,000	No cap, border 0.3 inch wide around checkering, 4 checks in top row, 5.5 diagonally on right top, 4 across bottom
Butt Plate with Cap and Plunger		
Springfield (C64283) Type 2	70,000 to end of production	Unmarked, cap, no border around checkering, 12 squares in vertical row running through screw holes, 6 full and 2 partial squares in row running through upper screw hole, 14 vertical diamonds x 7 horizontal diamonds on cap. Screw hole countersink 0.25 inch in diameter
Winchester Type 2	160,000 to end of Winchester production	May be marked on inside—beside cap—"2S." Shows a distinct border 0.20 inch from edge surrounding checkering, 12.5 squares in vertical row running through screw holes, 6 full squares in row running through upper screw hole, 14.5 vertical diamonds x 7 horizontal diamonds on cap. Screw hole countersink 0.3 inch in diameter

The M1 Garand

Manufacturer/ Type	Serial Number Range	Identifying Characteristics
Table 26, cont. **Butt Plate Identification Guide**		
International Harvester Type 2	All production	Similar to Winchester Type 2, without marking but diamonds more pyramidal in shape. Cap, distinct border 0.20 inch from edge surrounding checkering, 11.5 squares in vertical row running through screw holes, 14.5 vertical diamonds x 7 horizontal diamonds on cap. Screw hole countersink 0.31 inch in diameter
Harrington & Richardson Type 2	All production	Similar to Springfield Type 2. Cap, no border around checkering, 12 squares in vertical row running through screw holes, 6 full and 2 partial squares in row running through upper screw hole, 14 vertical diamonds x 7 horizontal diamonds on cap. Screw hole countersink 0.3 inch in diameter

The M1 Garand

HANDGUARD ASSEMBLIES

Handguard assemblies for the M1 Garand were manufactured in two parts of the same straight-grained American black walnut as the stock. The handguard assembly consisted of the 1) front and 2) rear handguards, 3) front handguard ferrule, 4) front handguard liner, 5) rear handguard band and 6) lower band and retaining pin.

M1 Garand handguards were always made in two pieces. Late experimental versions were manufactured in one piece of fiberglass but were never issued for service.

FRONT HANDGUARD

The front handguard assembly consisted of three pieces: 1) the front handguard (Figure 81A), 2) the front handguard liner (Figure 81B), and the front handguard ferrule (Figure 81C).

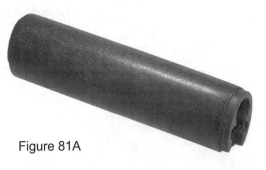

The front guard was milled from a solid piece of American black walnut—and in the mid-1950s from birch. Although the drawing number was changed from C46006 when used for the gas trap M1

Figure 81A

Garand to C64245 when used for the gas port M1 Garand from circa serial #50,000 to the end of production, there was no discernible difference between the two handguards themselves.

The front handguard was 7.4 inches long. It was 1.935 inches high by 1.510 inches wide at the rear and 1.790 inches high and 1.360 inches wide at the front. Both the front and rear had a lip (front—0.2 inch and rear—0.15 inch long) which fit into the front handguard ferrule and the lower band, respectively.

A hole was bored the length of the front handguard for the barrel. The hole was 1.890 inches in diameter at the rear and 1.70 inches in diameter at the front. A slot was also milled the length of the front handguard for the gas operating rod. The slot was 1.70 inches deep at the rear and 0.775 inch deep at the front by 0.570 inch wide. Front handguards for the gas trap M1 Garand were marked on the inside with the drawing number C46006. Front handguards for the gas port M1 Garands were not marked with the drawing number.

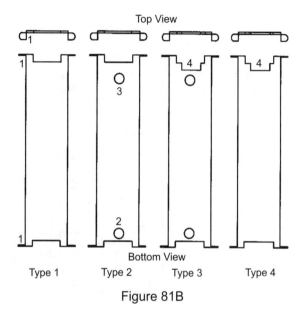

Figure 81B

Front Handguard Liner

The front handguard liner or spacer (drawing number B8893) was stamped from sheet steel and inserted into the front handguard and secured in place with tabs at the front and rear. It was used to prevent overheating during sustained, rapid fire. Four types of handguard liner were used, see Figure 81B and Table 27 for the differences (exaggerated).

The liner was 7.25 inches long, 0.645 inch wide and 0.025 inch thick. The sides were folded down to form a trough 0.280 inch deep. The four rounded tabs (1) on the front and rear of the handguard liner were 0.125 inch long with a radius of 0.240 inch. These tabs were bent outward at right angles. The rear tabs fitted into square notches at the end of the front handguard liner trough on the front handguard; the front tabs fitted through two slots on the front handguard ferrule and then were bent to fit into two semicircular depressions on the front surface of the front handguard.

The M1 Garand

The front handguard liner had two holes 0.150 inch in diameter centered on the flat top surface. The rear hole was centered 0.490 inch from the rear edge (2), the front hole 0.350 inch from the front edge (3). The front edge had a rectangular notch 0.70 inch wide by 0.15 inch deep cut away (4) to clear the Type 2 front handguard ferrule. Types 1 and 2 front handguard liners were blued, Types 3 and 4 were Parkerized.

Table 27 Front Handguard Liner Identification Guide (Inches)					
Type	Markings	Front Hole	Rear Hole	Notch	Serial # Range
1	B 8893	none	none	none	81-4,000 (Gas Trap Garands)
2	B 8898-1	0.350 from front edge	0.490 from rear edge	none	4,001-50,000 (Gas Trap Garands)
3	unmarked	0.350 from front edge	0.490 from rear edge	0.70 wide x 0.15 deep	50,001 to end of production (Gas Port Garands)
4	unmarked	none	none	0.70 wide x 0.15 deep	Late production and replacement

Front Handguard Ferrule

The front handguard ferrule was stamped from sheet steel, see Figure 81C. It capped the forward end of the front handguard and was secured to the front handguard liner by two tabs on the liner, refer to Figure 81B. The ferrule was 1.30 inches wide, 1.585 inches high and 0.260 inch deep and formed from sheet metal 0.0350 inch thick. The barrel hole was 0.630 inch in diameter. The rectangular opening to

Figure 81C

match the slot in the front handguard liner was 0.565 inch wide. Two semicircular indentations 0.16 inch wide by 0.260 inch high received the liner tabs.

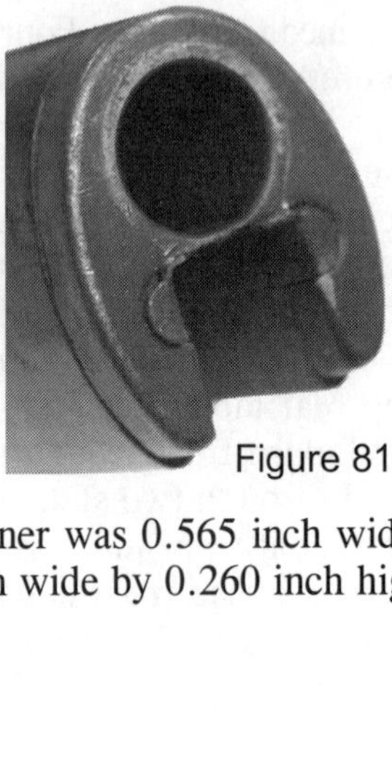

The M1 Garand

The **Type 1** front handguard ferrule for the gas trap M1 Garand was easily distinguished by a lip that protruded 0.156 inch from the front of the barrel hole. **Type 2** was manufactured for the gas port M1 Garand. It had a lip that protruded 0.06 inch from the rear of the barrel hole. All front handguard ferrules were Parkerized and unmarked.

REAR HANDGUARD

The rear handguard (drawing number C46024) was made of American black walnut 1.4 inches wide by 9.7 inches long and in the mid-1950s from birch, see Figure 82. The right side was relieved 0.4 inch deep by 5.6 inches long for the operating rod. Only the earliest rear handguards made for the M1 Garand gas trap rifles were stamped with the drawing number.

Figure 82

Two types of rear handguards were used and they are distinguished only by the clearance cut for the operating rod "handle" on the right rear side. The **Type 1** rear handguard did not have this clearance cut while the **Type 2** did (arrow). The clearance cut was made on the right rear in the form of an arc with a radius of 0.3 inch and 0.10 inch deep. Springfield changed from the Type 1 to the Type 2 rear handguard at circa serial #200,000 in the spring of 1941. Winchester did not change from the Type 1 to the Type 2 rear handguard until mid-1944 at circa serial #2,450,000.

NOTE: Many M1 Garand rear handguards, no matter their period of manufacture, will show the clearance cut at the rear. Ordnance maintenance personnel were instructed to make the clearance cut any time it was noted that the operating rod was binding against the wood. Also, this type of clearance cut may have been made with a knife or chisel and so will not always show a well-defined arc.

The rear handguard was grooved for the rear handguard band 1.9 inches from the rear. The groove was 0.05 inch deep by 0.36 inch

151

wide and ran horizontally across the handguard. A lip was cut 0.075 inch from the top of the wood and extended 0.20 inch forward on the front of the rear handguard. This lip slid into the rear of the lower band to secure the handguard at the front.

Rear Handguard Band

The rear handguard band was used to secure the after end of the rear handguard by snapping into grooves cut on either side of the barrel. Three types of rear handguard bands were used. The band was 0.05 inch thick by 0.355 inch wide. The ends bent at right angles were 0.25 inch long. They were drilled with a single hole 0.09 inch in diameter at each end. A punch or other tool could be inserted into these holes to pull them out of the barrel grooves and thus allow removal of the rear handguard without having to dismount the lower band, which was pinned in place with the solid or roll pin.

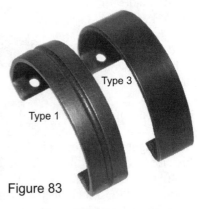

Figure 83

Type 1: This rear handguard band was milled from a casting, see Figure 83. It had an arched profile and a central groove 0.07 inch wide by 0.02 inch deep running its length. Very early versions (**Type 1A**) to circa serial #40,000 had the drawing number stamped on it. After, the drawing number was omitted on the **Type 1B** rear handguard band. The Type 1 was installed on Springfield M1 Garands to circa serial #780,000. Winchester used the Type 1 rear handguard band without the drawing number to circa serial #1,276,000.

Type 2: This rear handguard band was identical to the Type 1 handguard band in that it was milled from a casting, had the arched profile but did not have the central groove, refer to Figure 83. It was used for a short time only on Springfield M1 Garands circa serial #s 780,000-800,000. Winchester used the Type 2 from circa serial #s 1,276,000 to 1,380,000.

The M1 Garand

Type 3: This rear handguard band was stamped from sheet steel, had a flat profile, and no central groove. It resembled the Type 2 except that it was stamped from sheet steel rather than cast. It was used on Springfield M1 Garands from circa serial #790,000 to the end of production. Winchester used the **Type 3** rear handguard band from circa serial #2,305,000 to the end of production, including the so-called "Win-13" series, circa serial #s 1,600,000-1,640,000. International Harvester and Harrington & Richardson used only the **Type 3** rear handguard band.

LOWER BAND

The lower band, drawing number C46000, secured the front of the stock as well as the rear and front handguards to the rifle. It was designed to place a minimum of pressure on the barrel to eliminate any effect on accuracy. The lower band was 1.375 inches wide by 0.360 inch deep on its upper half and 0.190 inch wide on its lower half. See Figure 84.

The upper half contained a hole 0.725 inch in diameter for the barrel (A) and the lower half, a circular opening 0.695 inch in diameter for the operating rod (B). The lower third of the circumference was cut away. At the

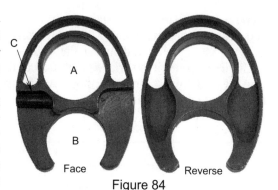

Figure 84

base of the upper hole was a rectangular boss with a hole 0.125 inch in diameter. The hole ran across the front of the lower band and held a pin 0.125 inch in diameter and 0.545 inch long. The pin (C) passed through the boss and a groove in the bottom of the barrel to hold the lower band in place. Lower band types are described below and in Table 28.

Three types of lower bands were manufactured and used on the M1 Garand. **Type 1A** was cast and milled to shape. It had a slightly arched outer surface and a center groove 0.070 inch wide

The M1 Garand

and 0.02 inch deep dividing the front and rear halves. Until circa serial #s 5,000-10,000 the drawing number was stamped on the side. The **Type 1B** lower band was used to circa serial #70,000 by Springfield and circa serial #1,200,000 by Winchester. It was identical to the Types 1A and B but lacked the drawing number. The Type 1 lower band can also be identified by "scallops" on either side of the lower hole partially enclosing the operating rod. Winchester used the **Type 1C** lower band which was cast and machined to shape but lacked the circumferential groove, from circa serial #1,200,000 to the end of production.

The **Type 2** lower band was stamped from sheet metal in two parts and brazed together. It lacked the circumferential groove but had a slightly rounded or "arched" outer surface at the top and sides. It was used by Springfield from circa serial #s 70,000 to 1,650,000. The Type 2 lower band did not have the scallops in the lower hole.

Type 3 lower bands were stamped from sheet metal in two parts and brazed together. They lacked the arched or rounded appearance of the Type 2 and had a flat profile. They were used by Springfield from circa serial #1,650,000 to the end of production. The Type 3 lower bands did not have the scallops in the lower hole. International Harvester and Harrington & Richardson also used the Type 3 lower bands.

Table 28 M1 Garand Lower Band Identification Guide			
Type	Marking	Serial # Range	Characteristics
Springfield			
1A	C 46000	81-5,000 to 10,000	Milled, arched profile, central groove, scallops
1B	None	5,000-10,000 to 70,000	Milled, arched profile, central groove, scallops
2	None	70,000-1,650,000	Stamped, arched profile, no groove, no scallops
3	None	1,650,000 to end of production	Stamped, flat profile, no groove or scallops

Type	Marking	Serial # Range	Characteristics
		**Table 28, cont.**	

Table 28, cont.
M1 Garand Lower Band Identification Guide

Type	Marking	Serial # Range	Characteristics
Winchester			
1B	None	100,001-1,200,000	Milled, arched profile, central groove, scallops
1C	None	1,200,000 to end of production	Milled, arched profile, no groove, no scallops
International Harvester			
3	None	All production	Stamped, flat profile, no groove or scallops
Harrington & Richardson			
3	None	All production	Stamped, flat profile, no groove or scallops

Lower Band Retaining Pin

The lower band retaining pin (arrow C in Figure 84) secured the lower band to the barrel. It penetrated a round slot in the lower band and passed through a notch cut in the bottom of the barrel.

Two types of lower band retaining pin were used. From the start of production to 1952, the pin was solid. From the 1952 to the end of production, a roll pin was used.

Both pins were 0.50 inch long by 0.125 inch in diameter.

CHAPTER 3
M1 GARAND TOOLS,
AMMUNITION AND ACCESSORIES

This section describes the items of equipment and ammunition that were considered to be "general issue" for the individual soldier, and certain other items that, while not "general issue," were a part of the combat infantryman's equipment, such as the M7 series of grenade launchers. The reader is referred to *Ordnance Tools, Accessories & Appendages of the M1 Rifle*, by Pyle, for further information regarding all accessories issued for the M1 Garand. See Appendix K.

OILER

The nickeled brass oiler and brass pull-through (Figure 85) developed for and issued with the Model 1903 Springfield, was standardized for the M1 Garand as well. After circa serial #70,000 when the butt trap was added to the stock, the oiler was carried in that compartment rather than in the soldier's pack. Two types were used that were basically alike except for tube materials.

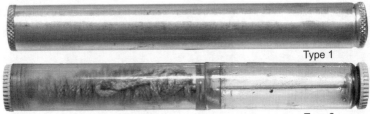

Type 1

Type 2

Figure 85

The **Type 1** oiler was a nickel-plated brass tube 6 inches long overall by 0.75 inch in diameter. The tube was divided into two sections, one for lubricant and the other for the brass pull-through/brush. Each end was closed by a screw cap. The oiler end cap had a wire "dripper" in the center. The other end cap had a leather pad on its outside surface to eliminate the sound of the oiler tube striking the inside of the butt plate trap door. The Type 1 oiler was issued to the end of 1942 when it was replaced with the Type 2 plastic oiler.

The M1 Garand

The **Type 2** oiler had a plastic case 5.9 inches long by 0.75 inch in diameter. It was divided into two sections, 1) lubricating oil and 2) pull-through. The clear tube allowed the soldier to see the level of oil. The Type 2 oiler was used from the beginning of 1943 to the end of production.

PULL-THROUGH AND BORE BRUSH

The pull-through consisted of two brass ends, a threaded brush and a "weight" to drop down the bore. The pull-through was developed and issued with the M1903 Springfield Rifle. The M1908 version was issued with the M1 Garand. The two ends were connected by waxed or varnished twine 2.5 to 3 feet long. The slotted patch holder was 0.220 inch in diameter by

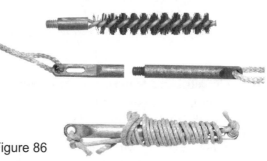

Figure 86

1.20 to 1.30 inches long. For storage, the two brass pieces were threaded together and the twine was wrapped around them, then inserted in the second compartment of the oiler tube, with the brush. See Figure 86.

In mid-1942, iron was substituted for the brass parts. The earliest iron parts were blued, but later were Parkerized until replaced in 1954 with the cleaning rod sets.

The "weight" measured 1.85 inches long and 0.220 inch in diameter. The bore brush had a brass body and the bristles were originally black, nonmetal. The brush was changed from a brass to an iron body in mid-1942, but with nonmetal bristles. During World War II, a mix of brass and nonmetal bristle bore brushes were issued. After World War II, the general-issue brush to the end of production was brass with brass bristles. The brush was 3.0 ± 0.125 inches long and 0.40 inch in diameter when the bristles were new.

The M1 Garand

BRUSH, CLEANING

This utility brush (Figure 87) fit into the butt trap with the combination tool and was used for general cleaning. The brush was 3.0 inches long by 0.50 inch high and 0.200 inch thick. The exact time period during which this brush was used is not known, but it was issued all during World War II. The bristles were black, nonmetal, and the top was metal, crimped over the bristles. Many are stamped with the manufacturer's name.

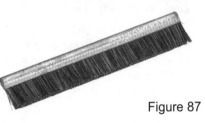

Figure 87

GREASE POT

Stoppages attributed to the lack of lubrication were ended by the issue of "lubriplate" grease in 1941, see Figure 88. It was contained in a small plastic cup with a screw-on lid (1). The cup measured 0.70 inch in diameter and 0.85 inch high. Originally, the grease was yellow in color. After the War, the grease was dark brown and did not separate as the yellow grease had (2). The cups were carried in the butt trap. Early cups had a curved edge around the bottom while late cups for the brown grease had sharp edges.

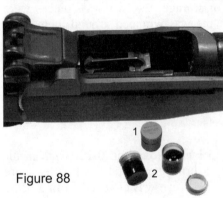

Figure 88

COMBINATION TOOL

The M3 Combination Tool was designed to provide the soldier with a basic tool to adjust the rear sight, assist in disassembling his rifle for cleaning and maintenance, and for making repairs. There were two basic types of combination tool.

The **Type 1** (M3) combination tool (Figure 89) had a single swiveling arm and performed five functions: 1) gas cylinder disassem-

The M1 Garand

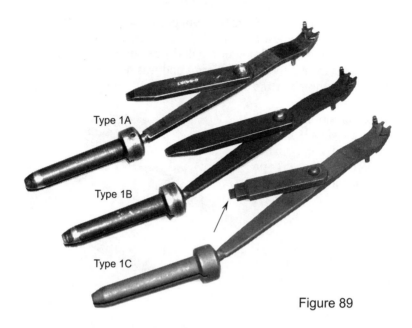

Type 1A

Type 1B

Type 1C

Figure 89

bly using a screwdriver blade; 2) spanner for setting tension on the rear sight nut; 3) follower arm pin punch; 4) slotted chamber cleaner; and 5) stuck case removal cup.

Three variations of the M3 tool were manufactured. The **Type 1A** was machined from bar stock and blued. It was marked with the part number, "C-64167." It was 2.75 inches long.

The **Type 1B** was similar to the Type 1A but was forged to shape, machined and then Parkerized. The Type 1B was not marked with the part number but may show a forging die number and letter. These were all made during World War II. Each Type 1B was 2.75 inches long.

The **Type 1C** was a modification of either the Type 1A or Type 1B. The screwdriver arm was reshaped (arrow) to better fit the "poppet" or Type 3 gas cylinder lock screw. The screwdriver arm was shortened by nearly 0.75 inch during the process to 2.0 inches in length.

The M1 Garand

The **Type 2** (M3A1) combination tool performed six functions, the same five as the Type 1 but with a chamber brush that replaced the slotted fork and the addition of a bolt disassembly head behind the brush. The Type 2 tool had two arms and was usually marked with the manufacturer's name or initials. See Figure 90.

Three variations of the Type 2 M3A1 combination tool were manufactured. The **Type 2A** had a screwdriver shaped like the Type 1A or Type 1B. Some early examples have been observed with a black bristle bush rather than the more common brass bristle brush. It was 2.30 inches long.

Type 2A

Type 2B

Figure 90

The **Type 2B** was made with a screwdriver redesigned to better fit the Type 3 "poppet" gas cylinder lock screw. All had brass bristle brushes. Each was 2.12 inches long.

The **Type 2C** combination tool was the Type 2A tool with the screwdriver modified like the Type 2B screwdriver so that it would better fit the Type 3 "poppet" gas cylinder lock screw. It was 2.0 inches long.

Figure 91

The **Type 3** (M10) combination tool was introduced in 1952 for use with the M1 Garand. When used in conjunction with the four cleaning rod sections, it performed four functions: 1) handle for the cleaning rod; 2) gas cylinder lock removal; 3) to set the tension on the rear sight; and 4) to disassemble the bolt. The M10 tool was Parkerized and there are no other known variations. It was 2.75 inches long, see Figure 91.

The M1 Garand

NOTE: Blued or black oxide-finished M10 tools have recently appeared on the market. These are reproductions. All original M10 tools were Parkerized.

Post-Korean War Cleaning Kit

In 1953, the pull-through and combination tool was replaced with a four-section steel cleaning rod and the M10 tool. The rod sections and tool were Parkerized. See Figures 92A and B. The four cleaning rod sections (1), patch and brass bore brush (2) fit into a 6-inch-long olive-drab bag, part #7267754, which slid into the top hole in the

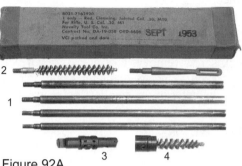

Figure 92A

buttstock, after the grease pot. The M10 tool (3) was placed in the section of the plastic oiler that previously held the thong and brush and the case was then inserted into the bottom stock hole. Each rod section was 6.30 inches long and 0.250 inch in diameter. The new chamber brush (4), part #7790582, would not fit into the butt trap and was carried

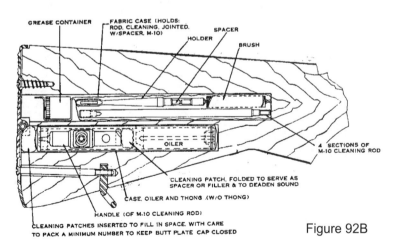

Figure 92B

161

in the pack or pocket. It was a brass bristle brush 2.75 inches long with a plastic assembly at the rear to rachet the brush. This same-style chamber brush was used to clean the shorter M14 chamber. A cleaning rod section screwed into the rear to use as a handle.

NOTE: The steel cleaning rods should only be used in conjunction with a muzzle guide to prevent wear on the muzzle end of the lands.

The M10 was a multifunction tool that could be used as a handle for the cleaning rods, as a bolt disassembly tool, a gas cylinder lock screw removal tool or a screwdriver. Its overall length was 2.75 inches and its diameter at the widest point was 0.590 inch. The diameter at the smallest point was 0.440 inch.

AMMUNITION

The production M1 Rifle was designed to use the Caliber .30 M1 Ball Cartridge, see Figure 93 (left to right: ball, tracer, armor piercing and practice cartridges). The M1 cartridge had a 172-grain boattail bullet driven to a muzzle velocity of 2,640 fps. After testing, there was some evidence that the M1 Ball cartridge with its heavy bullet placed excess stress on the rifle's moving parts during firing and would produce an unacceptable breakage rate. This concern led to the adoption of the Caliber .30 M2 Ball Cartridge which was loaded with a 150-grain flat-based bullet that provided a muzzle velocity of 2,700 fps, a round very simi-

Figure 93

lar to the original Caliber .30 Cartridge adopted in 1906 for the Springfield Rifle Model of 1903. Other than the weight of the bullet, the dimensions of the M1 and M2 Ball Cartridges were the same. See Tables 29 and 30 for descriptions and manufacturers.

The M1 Garand

Table 29 M1 Garand Ammunition, Caliber .30 M2 Ball		
Type	**Bullet, Type/Color**	**Usage**
Ball, M1	Plain tip	Withdrawn from service in 1940
Ball, M2	Plain tip	Personnel and target practice
Blank, M1909 (1)	Cardboard wad	Training and drill
Guard, M1906 (2)	Plain tip	Garrison duty
Gallery Practice (2)	Lead ball	Guard or practice
Dummy (3)	Plain tip	Mechanical training
Tracer	Red tip (early)	Observation or signaling
Tracer	Orange tip (late)	Observation or signaling
Armor Piercing	Black tip	Light armor targets
Incendiary	Light blue tip	Against flammable targets
Armor Piercing/Incendiary	Aluminum tip	Light armored flammable targets
Rifle Grenade	Case mouth crimped, no bullet	Used with the M7 series of Grenade launchers

1 Used with the blank adapter to cycle the action. Refer to Figure 95, below.
2 Not enough pressure to cycle the action. Bolt was operated manually.
3 Body of case was crimped or had holes drilled through it. Primer pockets were empty.

Table 30 Caliber .30 M1 and M2 Ammunition (.30-06 or 7.62 x 63 mm) Manufacturers' Headstamps	
Manufacturer	**Code**
Allegheny Ordnance Plant	AO
Denver Ordnance Plant	DEN
Des Moines Ordnance Plant	DM
Dominion, Canada	DAQ, DAL or D
Eau Claire Ordnance Plant	EC, changed to EW after Evansville Ordnance Plant startup

The M1 Garand

Table 30, cont. Caliber .30 M1 and M2 Ammunition (.30-06 or 7.62 x 63 mm) Manufacturers' Headstamps	
Manufacturer	**Code**
Evansville Ordnance Plant	EC
Evansville Ordnance Plant, Chrysler-Sunbeam	ECS
Frankford Arsenal	FA
Federal Cartridge Company	FC or FCC
Allegheny Ordnance Plant, Kelly-Springfield	KS
Lake City Ordnance Plant	LC or CN
Lowell Ordnance Plant	LM
Milwaukee Ordnance Plant	M
Peters Cartridge Company	PC, PCC or PCCO
Peters Cartridge Company—British contracts only	PC 1940
Remington Arms, Bridgeport, CT	RA or REM
Remington Arms, Hoboken, NJ	RA H
St. Louis Ordnance Plant	SL or BN
Twin Cities Ordnance Plant	TW
Utah Ordnance Plant	U or UT
Union Metallic Cartridge Company	UMC
United States Cartridge Company	USC or USCTG
Verdun (Canada)	VC
Western Cartridge Company	W, WC or WCC
Winchester Repeating Arms	WRA
NOTE: Military contract ammunition will have the manufacturer's code and the year of manufacture stamped on the head	

The head of the cartridge was stamped with the manufacturer's code and date of manufacture; for example, "Frankford Arsenal, FA 41," see Figure 94. Bullets other than ball were coded with different colors of paint. The paint covered approximately 0.25 inch of the tip of the bullet. Bullets and primers were sealed with a paint-type sealer to waterproof the ammunition. Table 30 lists manufacturers and their identifying headstamps.

The M1 Garand

The production-model M1 Garand used an "en-bloc" clip which held eight cartridges, see Figure 95.

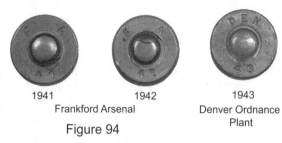

1941
Frankford Arsenal

1942

1943
Denver Ordnance Plant

Figure 94

When ammunition was issued to the soldier, it was already loaded into the clip. Without a clip, the rifle could only be fired by loading one round at a time directly into the chamber. Two basic types of clips were common to the M1 Garand. The **Type 1** en-bloc clip, developed and issued before World War II, was used with the gas trap and early gas port rifles. It had the clip latch detente cut all the way through the metal wall on either side (arrow 1). The **Type 2** en-bloc clip was used during World War II and after; the clip latch detente was not cut all the way through the metal wall but instead, formed an indentation (arrow 2). The clip measured 1.60 inches wide by 2.05 inches long at the base and 1.320 inches high. It was made of steel and given a spring temper. It held eight cartridges by spring tension.

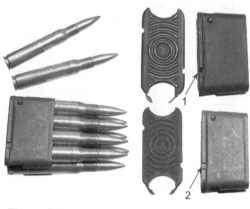

Figure 95

The clip was stamped with the manufacturer's initials or code on the bottom and Parkerized.

A variety of one-, two-, and five-round en-bloc clips for the M1 Garand are available. All are "commercial aftermarket," nonmilitary clips and are used for target shooting, competition shooting and hunting. A type of en-bloc clip has been sold as a "sniper clip" because it does not eject from an

The M1 Garand

M1C or M1D sniper rifle. No such clip was ever manufactured or standardized by the Ordnance Department.

M1 Garand Slings

Three different rifle slings were authorized for the M1 Garand rifle: 1) The Model 1907 Leather Sling, 2) the Model 1923 Canvas Web Sling and 3) the M1 Sling, Improved. The M1907 and M1923 were already in general service when the M1 Garand was adopted. The M1 Sling, Improved was adopted in 1943. Two variations of the M1907 and M1923 Slings were produced and five minor variations of the M1 Sling, Improved. The dimensions listed below are approximate due to shrinkage or stretching. Refer to Appendix I for instructions on installing slings.

Model 1907 Sling, Type 1

The M1907, **Type 1** sling was made from two 1.25-inch-wide leather straps connected with a "D" ring, see Figure 96. The sling had two leather keepers and all slings made were brown. The longer strap was 43 inches with a brass claw at one end. The strap had a double row of holes punched two-thirds of its length. The short strap was 25 inches long and had a brass claw at one end and the "D" ring sewn into a flap at the other. All hardware was brass which was chemically blackened to provide a "gunmetal" gray appearance. The slings were marked with the manufacturer's name or code and date of manufacture near one or both claws.

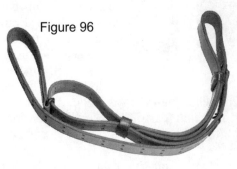

Figure 96

Model 1907 Sling, Type 2

The Model 1907, **Type 2** sling was identical to the Type 1 with the exception of the metal hardware which was Parkerized steel. The Type 2 sling was adopted in early 1942 when brass was declared a war-critical commodity.

The M1 Garand

Model 1923 Sling, Type 1
The Model 1923 **Type 1** sling was a canvas web, two-piece sling with two large buckles 1.30 inches wide. See Figure 97. It was quite difficult to install on the M1 Garand. The 46-inch-long strap had a buckle on one end and a metal cap on the other. The 28-inch strap had a "D" ring sewn on at one end and a metal cap at the other. A sliding lock on the long strap positioned the sling, and the short strap had a sliding buckle for adjustments. The M1923 sling was khaki in color, marked with the manufacturer's name and dated in ink, long since faded.

Model 1923 Sling, Type 2
The **Type 2** sling was identical to the Type 1 except that the color was changed from khaki to olive drab in mid-1943. Some Model 1923 slings observed have brass hardware finished to appear gunmetal gray while others have Parkerized steel fittings.

Figure 97

M1 Sling, Improved
The M1 Sling, Improved, Figure 98, was a single strap 46 inches long and 1.28 inches wide. A buckle was sewn on at one end and a metal cap was crimped onto the other. The butt end of the sling had

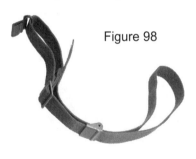

Figure 98

a flat metal snap hook to attach to the butt swivel of the stock. The other end had a sliding lock which secured the sling in position.

M1 Sling, Improved Type 1: The canvas webbing was khaki-colored with a narrow buckle measuring 0.85 inch wide, a small slide with a flat bottom surface, and was 0.45 inch thick. The hardware was Parkerized steel, although some end caps appear to have been blued. The **Type 1** was made in the first part of 1943 and was marked with the manufacturer's name and date in ink.

167

The M1 Garand

M1 Sling, Improved, Type 2: Identical to the Type 1 except that the canvas webbing was olive drab. Made from mid-1943 to 1945.

M1 Sling, Improved, Type 3: Identical to the Type 2 except that the sliding lock was redesigned to hold the sling tighter and not cut into the webbing. The new slide lock was 0.65 inch thick and had a ridge pressed into the bottom to accommodate a thicker locking tab. Made from 1945 to mid-1950s.

M1 Sling, Improved, Type 4: Identical to the Type 3 except that the buckle was made wider, measuring 1.3 inches wide. Some of the 1950s-period slings appear to have blackened brass hardware. Slings made in the late 1950s and early 1960s have more green in the webbing. Made from the mid-1950s to approximately 1970.

M1 Sling, Improved, Type 5: Identical to the Type 4 except that the strap material was changed from canvas to nylon. This sling saw limited use with the M1 Garand. The hardware was a greenish chemical-filmed steel. The nylon strap was made in brown or green. Some end caps are painted black. These slings were not marked.

M1 GARAND RIFLE BLANK FIRING ATTACHMENT

The M1 Garand blank firing attachment, made in two lengths, was a threaded cylinder covering the muzzle to trap sufficient gas in the bore to build up pressure to operate the gas piston and cycle the bolt. A small hole was drilled in the end to bleed off excess gas. See Figure 99.

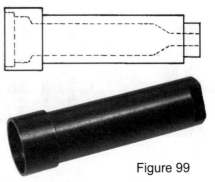

Figure 99

To install the blank firing attachment, the gas cylinder lock and screw were removed. The blank firing attachment was then slipped over the muzzle and threaded to the barrel. The gas cylinder lock screw was replaced.

The M1 Garand

The majority of blank firing attachments were blued, but some were Parkerized. The samples examined were unmarked. The U.S. Army did not standardize a blank firing attachment for the M1 Garand.

BAYONETS

The M1 Garand was designed to use the Model 1905 Knife Bayonet which was in service when the M1 was adopted. These bayonets had a 16-inch blade and wooden grip panels. They were originally manufactured at Springfield Armory (SA) or Rock Island Arsenal (RIA). Two types of the Model 1905 Bayonet were manufactured.

Model 1905 Bayonet, Type 1

Tens of thousands of M1905 bayonets had been manufactured before 1921. The most commonly issued scabbard for it was the canvas-covered, wooden-bodied Model 1910 Scabbard. Although the leather-covered Model 1905 Scabbard was still mentioned in the 1943 M1 Rifle Manual, they were rarely issued. See Figure 100.

The M1905 bayonet had a bright blade and a blued ricasso before 1917; after, the blades were Parkerized for their entire length. After World War I, thousands of the Model 1905 bayonets were refinished (Parkerized) to darken the blade, and reissued. All Model 1905 bayonets were also marked with the manufacturer's name or initials, were stamped with the date of manufacture and marked with a serial number that did not correlate to the rifle. Only a very few bayonets manufactured in early 1906 lacked a serial number.

Figure 100

The M1 Garand

Model 1905 Bayonet, Type 2

The Ordnance Department contracted with private companies in late 1941 to manufacture additional Model 1905-style bayonets—often referred to by collectors, erroneously, as the Model 1942. These differed from the Type 1 Model 1905 Bayonet in that they were all Parkerized, rougher in appearance and finish and were equipped with black or reddish plastic grips rather than wooden ones. The Model 1905, Type 2 Bayonets were not serial numbered but were dated either "1942" or "1943." An olive-drab fiberglass scabbard designated "M3" was issued with these bayonets. It was marked on the Parkerized metal throat with the Ordnance Department's flaming bomb symbol which contained the letters, "U.S." See Figure 101.

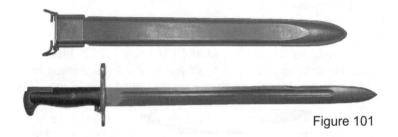

Figure 101

The following companies manufactured the Model 1905, Type 2 Bayonet: American Fork & Hoe (AFH), Oneida, Ltd. (OL), Pal Blade Company (PAL in an oval), Union Fork & Hoe (U.F.H.), Utica Cutlery Company (UC) and Wilde Tool & Drop Forge (WT). All were marked on the ricasso with the initials of the company over the initials "U.S." separated by the Ordnance Bomb

Figure 102

symbol, over the date. Figure 102 shows the style of markings on the Model 1905, Type 2 blades and scabbards.

The M1 Garand

Bayonet, M1

In mid-1943, a new bayonet for the M1 Garand was ordered with a shorter blade of 10 inches, see Figure 103. They were similar to the M1905E1 except that only the earliest production were marked with the date, 1943. The fuller was 5.75 inches long and began 3 inches from the point. The blade tip ended in a spear point; plastic grips, black or brownish in color, were installed. The Bayonet, M1 was identical to the Model 1905 Type 2 except for the shorter blade. The M7 fi-berglass scabbards were made for the Bayonet, M1 of ol-ive-green fiberglass with metal throats. The same compa-nies which made the M1905, Type 2 bayonet—with the

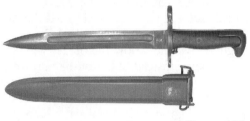

Figure 103

exception of Wilde Tool—manufactured the Bayonet, M1. One example has the Ordnance crossed cannon on the reverse of the ricasso and is marked "U.C." on the guard and latch bar.

Model 1905E1 Bayonet

In 1944-46, the Ordnance Department reduced the blade length of many 16-inch M1905 Types 1 and 2 bayonets to 10 inches by cutting off the tips, see Figure 104. The ends were then reground to either a spear or clip point. They can easily be distinguished by the fact that the fuller runs out past the tip. The wood grips were exchanged for black or reddish plastic grips. The modi-fied bayonets were Parkerized and stamped with the code of the contractor doing the work, on either the blade or handle. The M1905E1 can have any date or manufacturer. They were later reclassified as the Bayonet, M1. They were issued with the M7 scabbard. Many 16-inch M3 scabbards were also cut down to ac-commodate the shorter blade.

The M1 Garand

Figure 104

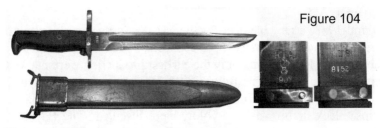

Bayonet, M5

In 1954, the bayonet for the M1 Garand was completely redesigned, see Figure 105. Designated the M5, it had a 7-inch knife blade similar to that used for the M1 Carbine, and guards of equal length above and below the blade, without the large circular ring for the bore. Instead, a button-like protrusion (1) was fitted to the upper guard. When the bayonet was mounted, the button slipped into the gas cylinder lock screw. Plastic checkered grip panels were installed and all metal parts were Parkerized. The bayonet stud lock mechanism (2) was controlled by a lever which protruded from the grip behind the lower guard.

The M5 bayonet was marked on the front of the guard vertically, on the left side of the blade, with "U.S. M5," "M5-1," or "M5A1."

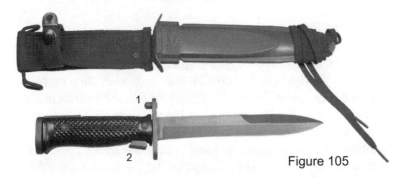

Figure 105

The front of the guard was marked with the manufacturer's name or initials: "AERIAL," "J&D TOOL CO," "IMPERIAL," "MILPAR COL," and "UTICA." One variation was marked only on the blade "Kiffe/Japan." The bottom forward face of the guard was stamped with the Defense Acceptance "eagle" stamp.

172

The M1 Garand

The M8A1 scabbard developed for the M3 combat knife and M4 Carbine bayonet was used, refer to Figure 105.

NOTE: Bayonets with 10-inch blades purportedly for the M1 Garand have appeared recently with a "bowie" clip point and finished blood groove. They are usually finished in black oxide. These bayonets were not made for the U.S. Armed Forces but may have been made by a foreign government for use with M1 Garands received as foreign aid, or else are an aftermarket product manufactured from bayonets purchased from a foreign government. Many thousands of M1 Garand bayonets and scabbards have been demilled and sold as scrap. Check any M1 Garand bayonet carefully for evidence that it has been rewelded—particularly in front of the guard—and refinished.

Modified Scabbards

Many fiberglass scabbards for the 16-inch-blade bayonets were modified (Figure 106) by shortening to accommodate the 10-inch blade. An original, unmodified scabbard will have a steel throat held to the fiberglass body by a tab on either side of the throat (1).

When the scabbards were modified, the tabs were cut off and after shortening, the throat was crimped onto the body (2).

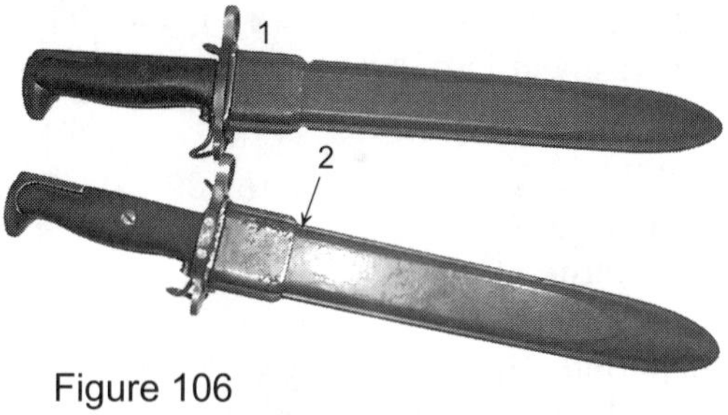

Figure 106

RUPTURED CASE EXTRACTOR

The ruptured, or broken, case extractor was issued to the soldier to remove cartridge cases from which the head had sheared off, rendering the rifle useless as a new round could not be inserted. The rear of the ruptured case extractor was shaped like the cartridge case head and the bolt extractor slid over it to lock in the cartridge groove. The front was smaller in diameter and had spring-loaded claws that gripped the inside of the headless case when inserted. The soldier simply chambered the ruptured case extractor like a cartridge, closed the bolt as far as possible to get a good "grip" on the inside of the case walls, then pulled the bolt handle to the rear, extracting the case. If the case was stuck so hard inside the chamber that it could not be extracted, the soldier then inserted a cleaning rod from the muzzle to drive out both the broken case and the ruptured case extractor.

Figure 107

The ruptured case extractor was made of steel, Parkerized and unmarked. The .30-06 Ruptured Case Extractor (Figure 107) was 3.25 inches long overall. The .30-06/7.62 mm NATO ruptured case extractor (Figure 108) was issued with M1 Garands in .30-06 and those converted to 7.62 NATO, and with the M14 rifle.

Figure 108

MUZZLE COVER

The muzzle cover (Figure 109) was adopted in mid-1943 and was designed to fit over the muzzle of the M1 Garand, M1 Carbine, Model 1903A3 and M1903A4 rifles. They were made of khaki-colored canvas and most examples are dated "1944." The strap circled the barrel and was held in place by snaps.

BARREL REFLECTORS

Figure 109

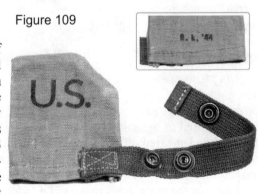

The construction of the M1 Garand did not permit inspection of the bore from the breech end simply by removing the bolt, as did the Model 1903 Springfield. A barrel reflector (Figure 110) similar to that developed for the M1903 (A) was issued. The barrel reflector was made of sheet brass, polished but not finished. It had a barrel length of 1.4 inch-

The M1 Garand

es, and smooth sides. From 1937 to 1942, there was a similar sheet brass barrel reflector but with a short barrel 0.65 inch long to make it easier to insert into the M1 Garand's chamber without having to depress the follower. It also had smooth sides (B). From 1942 through 1945, the barrel reflector was made of Parkerized steel and had three indenta-

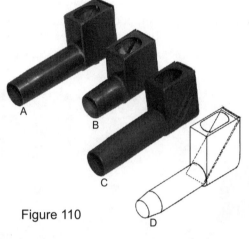

tions or ribs stamped into either side (C). Late post-World War II barrel reflectors were made of green plastic molded in two halves and held together by a screw. These last were used for both the M1 and M14 rifles.

The reflector case held a mirror at a forty-five-degree an-

Figure 110

gle (D). When the soldier placed the tubular end in the chamber, he could see along the bore through the eyepiece. The reflector body was 0.75 inch wide, 1.0 inch high and 0.50 inch thick. The chamber tube was 0.65 inch long. All three types had these same approximate dimensions.

CARTRIDGE BELTS AND POUCHES

The **Model 1910 Cartridge Belt** was manufactured to 1920 and was general issue at the time the M1 Garand was adopted. Two variations of this cartridge belt were used: the Model 1910 Dismounted (Infantry) Belt with ten ammunition pockets and the Model 1914 Mounted (Cavalry) Belt with nine pockets for rifle ammunition and a space on the left side for a clip pouch for the Government Model of 1911 .45 ACP Pistol ammunition, see Figure 111A. The adjustment buckles at the back faced outward from the ends of the belt, and the rear connecting strap had two claws at each end that locked into a double row of eyelets to hold the strap firmly in place. These belts were marked by the manufacturers and were khaki colored.

175

The M1 Garand

The **Model 1923 Cartridge Belt** was similar to the M1910 Dismounted Infantry Belt except that the design of the belt adjustment at the back was changed. The buckles were moved to the body of the belt to allow a tighter adjustment on thinner soldiers and the connecting strap passed through wide loops sewn to the back, which eliminated the metal claws and eyelets of the M1910/14 belt. Each of the ten pockets had an inner strap designed to separate the pair of five-round stripper clips for the M1903 series of bolt-action rifles. Very few Model 1923 Dismounted or Mounted

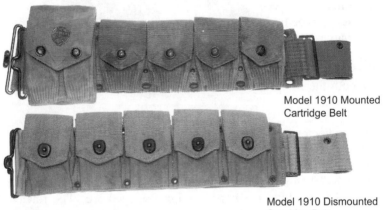

Model 1910 Mounted
Cartridge Belt

Model 1910 Dismounted
Cartridge Belt

Figure 111A

Belts were manufactured until 1940-41 when wartime production began. Originally khaki colored, these belts were dyed olive drab starting in mid-1943, see Figure 111B.

Model 1923 (Second Variation) Cartridge Belts were primarily manufactured into the late 1950s. As the bolt-action rifles had been retired from service, the Model 1923 belts were manufactured without the inner strap to separate five-round stripper clips. These later belts were all dyed olive drab and were dated from 1945 onward.

The Model 1938 Cartridge Belt was identical to the M1923 except that it had twelve pockets without the inner strap which was eliminated to allow the belt pockets to hold loaded M1 Garand

The M1 Garand

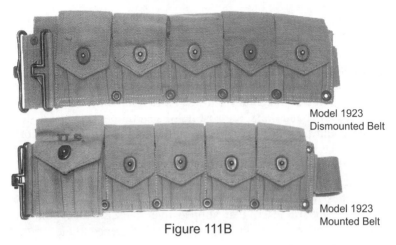

Model 1923
Dismounted Belt

Model 1923
Mounted Belt

Figure 111B

en-bloc clips. These belts were made for trial purposes and never entered general production. The belt was too long to fit thinner soldiers and the logistics of issuing two belts, one that could be used only with the M1 Garand, were not welcomed by the Ordnance Department.

M1 Garand Ammunition Pouch

Properly referred to as the "Pocket, Cartridge, Caliber .30, M1, Carbine or Rifle," it was a two-pocket belt pouch manufactured to hold two M1 Carbine magazines or two M1 Garand en-bloc clips. The pouch was so marked on the inner flap ("Pouch, Ammunition for M1 Carbine or Rifle"). When used in conjunction with the M1 rifle, this pouch was for garrison duty, see Figure 112 (A). They were dyed olive drab and were marked with the manufacturer's name and usually the date as well, on the inner flap.

A

B

Figure 112

Pouch, Ammunition, Universal

This pouch made for issue with the Browning Automatic Rifle, M1 Carbine, M1 Garand, and

177

The M1 Garand

later the M14 and M16 rifles. It held six M1 Garand clips, refer to Figure 112, (B).

Bandolier

In combat, soldiers were always issued extra ammunition. From the turn of the 20th century on, this extra ammunition was usually provided in "bandoliers" consisting of several pockets and a strap which could be worn over one shoulder and the neck. By World War II, the bandolier had evolved into a thin cotton shell consisting of six pockets and a carrying strap. The bandolier for the M1 Garand was 22.5 inches long and its strap was 41 inches long and 1.2 inches wide. Each pocket held one 8-round en-bloc clip and had a cardboard insert that slipped over the cartridge points to avoid tearing. A safety pin (blackened) was fastened to the strap; it could be used to take up excess slack in the strap or pin the bandolier strap or shell to the uniform jacket to keep it from flopping around and/or falling off the neck and shoulder. See Figure 113.

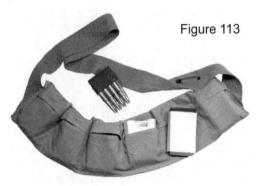

Figure 113

The bandolier was originally dyed khaki or brownish yellow but the color was changed to olive drab by 1945. The post-World War II bandoliers were marked on the outside with the ammunition type, maker and lot number. The earlier bandoliers were unmarked but had a cardboard insert in the left pocket with the information printed on it.

The U.S. Navy issued bandoliers with their converted M1 Garands (Mk. 2, Mk. 0 or Mk.1). They were marked "7.62 MM, NATO/ Ball, M80/8RD CLIPS/LOT XX XXXX." They can be distinguished from those bandoliers marked "7.62 MM, NATO" issued for the M14 Rifle by the fact that they specify "8RD CLIPS" whereas M14 bandoliers will specify "5RD CLIPS."

The M1 Garand

GRENADE LAUNCHER

When the M1 Garand was first adopted, only the M1903 Springfield rifle was used to launch grenades. Not until 1943 was a suitable grenade launcher, the M7, adopted for the M1 rifle, see Figure 114. To allow the use of the grenade launcher on the M1 Garand, the gas cylinder lock screw was redesigned with a valve that opened when the launcher was installed to allow propellant gases to escape and thus avoid excessive pressures. A pin mounted on the grenade launcher pressed the valve open to release excess propellant gases. A groove at the front of the launcher held a coil spring that secured the grenade in place. A special grenade-launching cartridge was adopted. All grenade launchers were Parkerized steel and clamped to the bayonet lug. Four variations of the M7 grenade launcher were developed and manufactured for issue.

Figure 114

The **M7** grenade launcher was of steel, milled to shape and Parkerized. The launcher had markings on the top from 1 through 6, indicating the range in hundred-yard increments. The bottom was marked with the manufacturer's name or initials, and "M-7 LAUNCHER/M1 RIFLE" or "M-7 GRENADE LAUNCHER/ FOR M1 RIFLE."

The **M7A1** grenade launcher was adopted in 1945. It was designed to allow the M1 Garand to fire in the semiautomatic mode

The M1 Garand

with the grenade launcher installed. The M7A1 was cast with the outer diameter machined to the specified tolerances. It attached to the rifle with the same locking hinge as the M7. It was manufactured only at the Rock Island Arsenal and was marked on the right side, "LAUNCHER, GRENADE M7A1" and on the left, "RIA 7313299."

The **M7A2** grenade launcher was a post-World War II development and identical to M7A1 with the exception of the area above the muzzle which was enlarged to provide more support to the new Type 3 gas cylinder lock. During its production run, the tension spring was changed to a clip-type retainer spring. It was manufactured only by K.R. Wilson of Arcade, New York, and was marked on the right side, "LAUNCHER, GRENADE M7A2" and on the left, "KRW C-7265949."

The **M7A3** grenade launcher was the same as the M7A2 except that the body was lengthened to add three additional range rings for a higher velocity and flatter trajectory. M7A3 grenade launchers were manufactured with the clip-style retainer and a few were equipped with a hinged sight that folded when not in use. The M7A3 was used with the M1 Garand to its end of service. They were marked on the left side with the manufacturer's initials or name and the part number, "726617," and on the right, "LAUNCHER, GRENADE M7A3." The Defense Department Acceptance stamp usually follows the part number.

Dummy Rifle Grenades
A large selection of rifle grenades suitable for use with the M1 Garand exists, most of which are not legal for individuals to possess. The study of rifle grenades was therefore beyond the scope of this text and so we will mention only the two commonly encountered "dummy" practice rifle grenades. The earlier of the two was the M11 series which was 11 inches long and painted black with white identification markings on the body. The M31 series was 17 inches long and larger in diameter than the M11 series. It was painted blue with white markings. The M31 series was also used with the M14 rifle.

The M1 Garand

Model	Manufacturer
Table 31 **M7 Series Grenade Launcher** **Manufacturers**	
Model	**Manufacturer**
M7	Arrow-Hart Fay & Scott Hawley Smith Machine Company International Business Machines Knapp Monarch Mitchell & Smith, Inc.
M7A1	Rock Island Arsenal
M7A2	K.R. Wilson
M7A3	Acme Machine Works K.R.Wilson Long Manufacturing Division Sun Ray Photo, Inc.

For a more detailed study of M1 Garand accessories, the authors highly recommend, *Ordnance Tools, Accessories & Appendages of the M1 Rifle,* by Billy Pyle. See Appendix K.

APPENDIX A
M1 GARAND SERIAL NUMBERS
BY MONTH AND YEAR

The serial number listings by month presented below were developed by Scott Duff, a recognized authority on and author of a series of books on the M1 Garand (see Bibliography, Appendix K). They are reprinted here with his kind permission.

Year/Month	Serial #, Month End	Year/Month	Serial #, Month End
Springfield Armory 1932-34 80		April	10,703
1937		May	11,511
August	120	June	12,848
September	307	July	12,911
October	539	August	14,823
November	696	September	17,010
December	1,034	October	19.410
1938		November	21,293
January	1,186	December	23,567
February	1,338	**1940**	
March	1,809	January	26,729
April	2,213	February	30,008
May	2,406	March	33,790
June	2,911	April	38,034
July	2,911	May	41,679
August	3,537	June	46,221
September	4,386	July	51,970
October	5,242	August	59,868
November	6,072	September	68,054
December	6,972	October	78,306
1939		November	90,177
January	7,715	December	100,000 & 165,501 to 168,073
February	8,762		
March	9,893		

The M1 Garand

Year/Month	Serial #, Month End	Year/Month	Serial #, Month End
1941		March	1,469,177
January	183,519	April	1,547,452
February	197,811	May	1,629,565
March	211,228	June	1,710,012
April	228,727	July	1,786,469
May	248,757	August	1,877,654
June	269,686	September	1,978,407
July	296,252	October	2,092,825
August	324,301	November	2,204,430
September	349,442	December	2,305,849 & 2,410,000 to 2,420,191
October	377,258	**1944**	
November	401,529	January	2,543,412
December	429,811	February	2.634,316
1942		March	2,723,004
January	462,737	April	2,810,312
February	498,216	May	2,900,312
March	542,494	June	2,981,126
April	588,879	July	3,051,952
May	638,679	August	3,114,434
June	691,401	September	3,180,532
July	749,779	October	3,242,497
August	809,016	November	3,202,641
September	872,343	December	3,359,159
October	940,250	**1945**	
November	1,008,899	January	3,450,503
December	1,909,310	February	3,521,489
1943		March	3,627,442
January	1,169,091	April	3,717,867
February	1,200,000 & 1,357,474 to 1,396,255	May	3,797,768

The M1 Garand

Year/Month	Serial #, Month End
June	3,875,601
July	Unknown
August	Unknown
September	Unknown
October	3,888,081
Winchester Repeating Arms Company	
1941	
January	100,101 100,501
February	100,831
March	102,701
April	104,901
May	107,801
June	111,501
July	115,501
August	120,111
September	122,081
October	126,130
November	131,130
December	137,960
1942	
January	144,110
February	149,130
March	155,310
April	162,190
May	165,500 also 1,200,001 to 1,203,692
June	1,210,472
July	1,218,972

Year/Month	Serial #, Month End
August	1,228,982
September	1,241,002
October	1,254,002
November	1,266,502
December	1,276,102
1943	
January	1,282,762
February	1,294,762
March	1,309,772
April	1,323,872
May	1,336,882
June	1,349,982
July	1,364,982
August	1,380,000 also 2,305,850- 2,305,932
September	2,318,032
October	2,334,032
November	2,349,632
December	2,364,642
1944	
January	2,379,642
February	2,394,642
March	2,409,642
April	2,424,642
May	2,439,642
June	2,454,642

The M1 Garand

Year/Month	Serial #, Month End
1945	
January	2,534,232 also 1,600,000 to 1,605,600
February	1,607,100
March	1,613,000
April	1,620,000
May	1,627,000
June	1,640,000

M1 Garand collectors may note some duplication of Springfield and Winchester serial numbers, particularly in the 2,305,800 to 2,533,400 range.

No monthly range of serial numbers has yet been developed for post-World War II production of the M1 Garand. Following are the serial number blocks assigned to Springfield Armory and the two prime contractors, International Harvester and Harrington & Richardson Arms.

M1 Garand Post-World War II Manufacture Serial Number Ranges		
Manufacturer	Serial # Range	Quantity
Springfield	4,200,001-4,399,999 5,000,000-5,000,500 5,278,246-5,488,246 5,793,848-6,099,905	1,999,998 500 210,000 306,057
International Harvester	4,440,000-4,660,000 5,000,501-5,278,245	220,000 277,744
Harrington & Richardson	4,660,001-4,800,000 5,488,247-5,793,847	139,999 305,600

APPENDIX B
M1 GARAND SNIPER RIFLES
THE M1C, M1D AND MC 1952 SNIPER RIFLES

The first mention of an M1 Garand equipped with a telescopic sight occurs in *Book of the Garand*, by Major General Julian S. Hatcher. It appears in a section describing the Garand in use during World War II, written by Colonel W.J. Whaling, USMC. Colonel Whaling, in describing the use of the M1 Garand by marines and soldiers on Guadalcanal and in the Southwest Pacific theater, wrote, "Eighteen telescope-sighted Garands came ashore with the Fifth Marine Regiment when it landed at Guadalcanal on August 7, 1942. These were at a premium, as they were most useful for the snipers." Unfortunately, he does not describe these "telescope-sighted" M1 Garands any further and we have no idea what kind of telescopic sight was used or how they were mounted.

Not until late 1944 was a standard-issue sniper version of the M1 Garand developed, one fitted with a standard-issue telescopic sight. Because the en-bloc clip was inserted through the top of the receiver, and empty cartridges and the empty clip were also ejected through the top, the telescopic sight had to be offset on its mount to the left. To bring the shooter's eye into proper alignment, a leather cheek pad was attached to the stock with two brass screws and leather laces.

Three variations of the M1 sniper rifle were developed and standardized for general issue. The first was the M1C, adopted as standard on July 27, 1944, and which employed a Griffin & Howe-developed mount for the Lyman Alaskan telescopic sight, which was classified as the M81 or M82 Telescope in military service. A total of 7,971 were built.

The second was the M1D which was adopted as a substitute standard in September 1944. The M1D used a specially designed barrel mount developed by John C. Garand to hold the M84 Telescopic Sight. The M84 was an improved M81/82. All M1Ds were built using standard service rifles between 1951 and 1962-63. Few saw service during the Korean War but they were used in the many military actions U.S. forces engaged in between 1953 and the late 1960s, including Lebanon (1958) and the Dominican Republic (1965) and during the war in Vietnam. The M1Ds will show barrel dates between early 1952 and early 1953.

The third variation was the MC 1952 Sniper Rifle developed by the U.S. Marine Corps. It was equipped with the Stith-Kollmorgen 4X telescopic sight in the Griffin & Howe Mount. The MC 1952 Sniper

The M1 Garand

M1C Sniper rifle with M82 telescopic sight and M2 Cone Flash Hider, North Cape Publications collection.

M1D Sniper rifle with M84 telescopic sight and M2 Cone Flash Hider, North Cape Publications collection.

M1D Sniper rifle with M84 telescopic sight and T37 Prong Flash Hider. Note the nonregulation serial number painted on the telescopic sight bracket. Craig Riesch collection.

The M1 Garand

Rifles were essentially M1C sniper rifles rebuilt at Springfield to Marine Corps specifications from 1952 to 1962.

THE M81 AND M82 TELESCOPIC SIGHTS AND MOUNTS

Two variations of the commercial Lyman Alaskan 2.2 fixed power telescopic sight were standardized by the Ordnance Department and designated the M81 and M82 for use on the M1C. The M81 telescopic sight had a crosshair reticle while the M82 scope had a tapered post reticle. See Figures B-1A and B-1B.

Adjustments to elevation and windage were made by removing two screw-on caps from the adjustment housing. Two dial screws were turned to move the reticle up or down, left or right to center the point of aim. The M81 and M82

Figure B-1A. M82 Telescopic Sight

barrels were 0.875 inch in diameter and 10.8 inches long. All M81 and M82 barrels and Griffin & Howe mounts and brackets were originally blued.

The eyepiece was covered with a

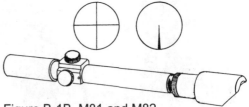

Figure B-1B. M81 and M82 Telescopic Sight Reticles

rubber shield designed to provide both a brighter sight picture by eliminating ambient light, and to correctly position the shooter's eye. The rubber shield was 1.41 inches in diameter and 1.970 inches long overall and 0.185 inch thick. A tubular sheet metal sunshade was added to the front of the barrel to improve the sight picture by reducing ambient glare and to prevent the objective lens from casting glints that would reveal the shooter's position. The sunshade telescoped the barrel and could be extended or withdrawn. Eye relief of the scope was 5 inches.

The M1 Garand

The M81 was marked on the left side of the barrel, "TELESCOPE M81/SERIAL NO. XXXXX/STOCK NO. 64373." It had a crosshair reticle and the scope tube was originally blued.

The M82 was marked on the left side of the barrel, "TELESCOPE M82/SERIAL NO. XXXXX/STOCK NO. 84374." Later M82s manufactured after 1948 show the Federal Stock Number "F001-0084888." Elevation and windage adjustment housings were both marked "7634671." The eyepiece was marked "7634670" and the objective lens retaining ring was marked "7575050." Elevation and windage adjustment caps were marked "7575180." Lyman manufactured both the M81 and M82 telescopic sights, but the M82 was also manufactured by Wollensack Optical Company, Rochester, New York.

The mounting assembly for the M81 and M82 was designed by Griffin & Howe, Inc., of New York (see Figure B-2) and used to mount the telescopic sight on the M1C. The assembly was attached to a bracket (drawing number C7312600) affixed to the left side of the M1 receiver. The bracket was 4.03 inches long by 0.501 inch wide and serial numbered to the receiver on the front, outer surface or bottom. Two locating pins (drawing number B7312603) and three socket head screws (drawing number B7312607) attached the bracket to the receiver. Two pin holes and three screw holes drilled and threaded on the left side of the receiver received them.

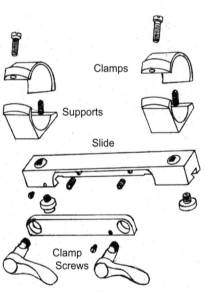

Figure B-2. Griffin & Howe Mount Assembly for the M1C Sniper Rifle

After the bracket was installed on the receiver, the three screws were staked with a small punch around their circumference.

The telescope was attached to the bracket by a slide 3.825 inches long by 0.620 inch wide and 0.445 inch high (drawing number C7312613), serial numbered to the receiver and bracket. The slide was

The M1 Garand

grooved on the bottom to slip over the bracket and was held in place by a spring-loaded clamp (drawing number B7312601) which was positioned by two stops (drawing number B7312615) 0.230 inch long and secured with two clamp screws 1.280 inches long (drawing number B7312606) and which rotated clockwise to engage the bracket. The clamp springs were drawing number B7312601.

The telescopic sight tube was attached to the slide by supports and clamps 0.625 inch wide, that were offset to the left (drawing number C7312616). The supports were held to the slide by two screws (B7312609 and B7312610). The clamps were attached to the supports with four machine screws (drawing number B7312623).

While the Griffin & Howe bracket and slide were serial numbered to the rifle on which they were originally attached, the telescope tube was not. It was marked with its own serial number which did not relate to either the mount or the rifle.

Mounts made and delivered by September 1945, according to the original contract, were marked: "GRIFFIN & HOWE, INC. NEW YORK/PAT. # 1,856,549 MAY 3, 1932." Mounts delivered during the Korean War were marked: "FSN 1240-647-1107/MOUNT, TELESCOPE/GRIFFIN & HOWE, INC./U.S." These late mounts were supplied after 1948 when Federal Stock Numbers (FSN) were first assigned. They were also used for the MC 1952.

At the end of the war in Europe, government records, according to Scott Duff, the well-known authority on the M1 Garand, show that some M1C rifles were rebuilt in Europe. During the Korean War, a total of 4,796 M1Cs still in inventory were rebuilt between July 1, 1951 and June 30, 1953. Many were reequipped with the M84 Telescopic Sight, but the M81 and the M82 were also used, as was the commercial Lyman Alaskan variation. The Lyman "Alaskan" magnification was specified as 2.5X. It was equipped with the rubber eyecup but not the sunshade. Finally, a total of 1,500 M1C receivers were returned to service as standard infantry rifles by plugging the bracket mounting holes during November-December 1952.

THE M84 TELESCOPIC SIGHT AND MOUNT

The M84 telescopic sight was developed early in 1945 and standardized in March 1945 for the Model 1903A4 Sniper Rifle to replace the M73B1, see Figures B-3A and 3B. It was adopted for the M1D Garand Sniper Rifle in January 1951. The M81/82 scope was redesigned by the Artillery Development Division at Frankford Arsenal to include rubber gaskets to

The M1 Garand

ensure a waterproof scope, enlarged adjusting dials and flip-open rectangular caps that replaced the screw-on caps that were so easily lost. The reticle combined the crosshair with the tapered post. The M84 telescope barrel was 0.875 inch in diameter by 10.8 inches long. The M84 was also equipped with a rubber eyecup to position the shooter's eye at the proper distance. Libby-Owens-Ford built the majority of the M84 telescopic sights.

The M84 mounted to the M1D Garand

Figure B-3A and B-3B M84 Telescopic Sight and Reticle

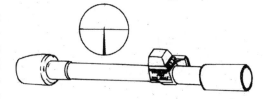

in an entirely different manner than its predecessors, see Figure B-4. A sturdier barrel mount that did not require drilling through the side of the receiver was developed by John C. Garand late in 1944 and Patent No. 2,449,551 for the mount was issued September 21, 1948. It consisted of the base (C7312541) which fitted over a machined section of the M1 barrel (D7312555)—just ahead of the receiver face—and held in place with a taper pin that was staked at the 12, 3, 6, and 9 o'clock positions. Some mounts will show a square notch directly below the threaded mounting hole. Most M1D mounts were manufactured by the Marc A. Porter Company of Hartford, Connecticut, between 1951 and 1953. The M1D mount was not marked in any way.

A removable bracket (C7312542) attached to the base with a spring-loaded screw attached in turn to a knurled knob. The M84 telescopic sight was held in the bracket by a hinge piece (B7312543) which attached to the bracket with a pin and two Allen hex-head machine screws. The sight could be removed and replaced on the mount without losing its zero.

NOTE: Fake M1D mounts have appeared on the market but can be distinguished from the authentic M1D mount by the following character-

The M1 Garand

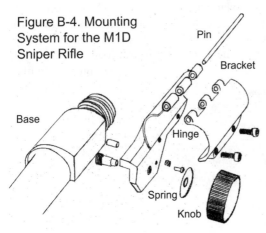

Figure B-4. Mounting System for the M1D Sniper Rifle

Pin

Bracket

Base

Hinge

Spring

Knob

istics: 1) the casting is rough and not well finished particularly in the hinge area, 2) the screw holes in the hinge piece are not countersunk, 3) the right screw hole is drilled through the mount bracket and 4) the spring-loaded plunger that locks the mount to the barrel is usually not installed, refer to Figure B-4.

The M84 was marked on a separate label plate attached with screws to the right side of the adjustment housing, beneath the elevation adjustment cover, "TELESCOPE/M84/SERIAL NO. XXXX." On early examples, the serial number was enclosed in a rectangle, but on late examples it was not. The serial number was added separately with a stamping machine or by hand before the label plate was affixed to the telescope. All M84 telescope barrels were originally finished in blue or black oxide. Mount and bracket were Parkerized. The M1D mount and bracket assembly are unmarked and were not serial numbered to the rifle on which they were originally mounted. Some M1Ds have been observed with the rifle's serial number painted on the bracket, probably by the unit to which they were issued.

Lyman Alaskan Telescopic Sight

There are indications that the Lyman Alaskan telescopic sight may have been the original sight mounted on the M1C Garand in 1945.

Lyman Gun Sight Corporation's Alaskan telescopic sight had been ordered for mounting on the Model 1903A4 Sniper Rifle as a replacement for the Weaver M73B1 (330C) telescopic sight. Remington even delayed final assembly of the M1903A4 for a short time while waiting for the Alaskan sights to be delivered. But all of Lyman's Alaskan production was being used for other purposes including the M1C sniper rifle program, see Figure B-5.

The M1 Garand

Figure B-5. Top: Lyman Alaskan Telescopic Sight with Ordnance Department part numbers and commercial markings; below: M81 telescopic sight with commercial Lyman and Ordnance Department markings.

Four variations of the "military" Alaskan telescopic sight have been observed: 1) The M73E1 with the Ordnance Department's part number, "7634671," stamped on the windage and elevation adjustment housings, "7674029" on the scope tube or body, and "7634670" on the eyepiece plus Lyman's commercial markings. 2) The M81 in two variations, one with the Lyman commercial markings but stamped "M81" and 3) the M81, marked "M81" without Lyman commercial markings and 4) the M82, marked "M82," also without Lyman commercial markings.

The Alaskan telescopic sight was "militarized" as the M81 and M82 in 1945 and the postwar years. The majority of the standard Lyman Alaskan commercial telescopic sights acquired by the Ordnance Department in 1944-45 appear to have been reissued for use on the Model 1903A4 sniper during and after the Korean War. Those marked "M81" and "M82," usually without commercial markings, appear to have been installed on the M1C Garand during the Korean War.

Stith-Kollmorgen 4XD MC-1 Telescopic Sight

In 1951, the U.S. Marine Corps reviewed the status of their sniper rifle equipment and decided to standardize on the M1C. Marine Corps snipers used the M1C extensively in Korea, along with the 1940s vintage Model 1903A1 rifle equipped with the Unertl 8X scope. Sniper rifles were issued to specially trained Marines designated Scout-Snipers. Most of their M1Cs were originally built in late 1944 through early 1945, and were rebuilt in 1952-53 at Springfield at the Corps' request. The M1C was the official Marine Corps sniper weapon during the Korean War, although a small number of M1Ds were also used. The M1C and the M1D continued in use by the Marine Corps well into the war in Vietnam when they were replaced as the official sniping weapon by the M40, a bolt-action rifle hand-built by Marine Corps armorers at Quantico on Remington Model 700 BDL frames.

The same 1951 review recommended that the Marine Corps also procure a new telescopic sight that was an improvement on the

The M1 Garand

M81, M82 and M84. The telescopic sight chosen was the Stith BEAR CUB, designed by the Stith Optical Company and manufactured by the Kollmorgen Optical Corporation. It was a fixed-focus 4X scope 11 inches long and 1.250 inches in diameter with a 3- to 4-inch eye relief. The telescope tube was marked "STITH MOUNTS S.A. TEX./4X DOUBLE/ KOLLMORGEN OPTICAL CORP/BROOKLYN N.Y./PAT. PEND." The Marine Corps also stamped on the top or side of the tube "MC" followed by a serial number. On some tubes, the property mark "U.S." and the Federal Stock Number were also marked. The telescope tubes were made of aluminum and were finished in black enamel. Storm Queen commercial-molded rubber eyecups were also furnished.

The scope was mounted on a variation of the Griffin & Howe mount enlarged to enclose the larger-diameter tube. The mount fitted the original M1C bracket. The clamps were enlarged to 1.250 inches in diameter. The slide and bracket were not serial numbered to the rifle. The slide was marked "FSN 1240-647-1107/MOUNT, TELESCOPE/ GRIFFIN & HOWE, INC./U.S."

SNIPER RIFLES—PERIOD OF USE

The M1C was developed starting in 1943. It was standardized on July 27, 1944 and at the same time, a contract was let to Griffin & Howe, Inc., to produce a total of 37,000 mount assemblies. They delivered 14,000 by May 1945, and 21,000 more by the end of the war on August 12, 1945. The production M1C rifles first appeared in early 1945. Most if not all M1Cs seem to have been made up from production rifle receivers that were manufactured within a ten-month period, August 1944 to May 1945. Barrel dates as early as 4-44 have been noted, suggesting that barrels were drawn from inventory as well as from new production. Production records indicate that 6,896 M1C sniper rifles were built at Springfield Armory by the end of the war in August 1945. A small number of M1Cs were built in 1946 and 1947 as well. Very, very few M1Cs reached combat troops in either the European or Pacific Theaters.

The M1C was the principal sniper rifle during the Korean War, along with the M1903A4. A large number of the M1C rifles were refurbished during the Korean War. Most of these will show 1945-manufactured receivers but barrels dated between 1-51 and 4-52. Keep in mind that both M1C and M1D rifles were still in U.S. Army inventory as late as mid-1995 and underwent a great number of changes and rebuilds during their service lives. All M1Cs built in the January to May 1945 period should show parts in use at that time and the M81 or M82 scope. Keep

The M1 Garand

in mind that as parts could remain in parts bins for two to three months before being used, parts manufactured as early as October of 1944 can be expected. Those refurbished during the Korean War (1950-53) may show a mixture of parts in use during that time. Many M1Cs were reequipped with the M84 scope during this rebuild period.

The M1D was built in very small quantities in 1944 for test purposes. The majority of M1D Sniper Rifles were built using standard M1 Garand rifles during and after the Korean War, primarily in the 1960s by armorers at all levels using barrels produced at Springfield Armory between January 1952 and February 1953. While the M1D served only as a "supplemental sniper rifle" to the M1C and probably saw very little if any combat service during the Korean War, they continued in use well into the war in Vietnam and were used by both American and South Vietnamese forces.

The M1952MC Sniper Rifles with the Stith-Kollmorgen scopes were manufactured in 1952-53 and continued in use from 1954 through 1962. They saw no use during the Korean War. In 1962, all M1C and M1952MC sniper rifles were declared obsolete by the Marine Corps. However, they still saw wide use in Vietnam in the early 1970s.

All M1Cs, M1Ds and M1952MCs were fitted with a leather cheek pad. Those originally fitted to the M1C in the 1945 period were manufactured by Kayline and are marked with a decorative "K" stamped into the leather. They are undated. Those manufactured and installed on M1Cs, M1Ds and M1952MCs during the Korean War period were marked "MRT" and show the date they were installed, stamped and marked in ink.

The M1C, M1D and M1952MC sniper rifles were also equipped with flash hiders. From late 1944 to the mid-1950s, the M2 flash hider was used. Its mounting bracket made of rolled steel or stamped sheet steel was similar to that used with the M7 Grenade Launcher. It had a truncated cone made of sheet steel attached to the muzzle end. The M2 was replaced by the T37 flash hider in 1958. It had four prong-like fingers, open in front, and a threaded band that screwed onto the barrel in place of the gas cylinder lock. In the mid-1960s, a small ring was added to close the four fingers which had an annoying tendency to tangle in brush.

Tables B-1 through B-4 present identifying characteristics of the M1C, M1D and M1952MC Sniper Rifles.

The M1 Garand

Table B-1 Specifications U.S. Rifle, Caliber .30, M1C and M1D	
Length of Rifle, no flash hider	43.60 inches
Length of Rifle, with flash hider	46.13 inches
Weight of Rifle with telescopic sight and cheek pad, but not web carrying case, M65	11.81 pounds
Weight of telescope, M81 or M82 only, with removable mount assembly and eyeshield	1.24 pounds
Weight of flash hider	0.44 pound
Weight of web sling	0.26 pound
Weight of cheek pad	0.34 pound
Weight of rifle M1C or MID without accessories but including permanently mounted bracket	9.75 pounds
Weight of leather sling, M1907	0.50 pound
Weight of telescope, M81 or M82 only, without removable mount and including rubber eyeshield	0.84 pound
Weight of web carrying case, M65	0.28 pound
Trigger pull	6.5 pounds maximum, 4.5 pounds minimum
Focus for distance	Universal
Maximum useful range	800-1,000 yards
Zero setting range (telescope)	300 yards
Field of vision at 100 yards	35 yards
Magnification	2.2X
Eye relief, telescope (approximately)	5 inches
Weight of rifle, MIC or MID, complete with accessories in a V3C corrugated fiberboard box	15.5 pounds
Overall dimensions of chest	13 7/8 x 11 1/8 x 35 1/2 inches

Table B-2 M1C Sniper Rifle Identifying Characteristics	
Manufacturer	Springfield
Receiver	Part no. D2829135-35
Serial Number Range	3,160,000-3,800,000
Barrel Date	4/44 to 5/45 and 1/51 to 4/52

The M1 Garand

Table B-2, cont. M1C Sniper Rifle Identifying Characteristics	
Telescopic Sight/Magnification	M81 or M82; M84 may be used after 1950/ 2.2X
Base	Serial Numbered (1)
Clamps or Rings	Serial Numbered (2)
Stock Cartouche	S.A./G.A.W. and S.A./N.F.R.
Cheek Pad	Leather, "K" marked and undated before 1951, dated after and marked "MRT"
Flash Hider	M2 Flash Hider before 1958, T37 after

1 Data based on 100 M1C Rifles auctioned by Director, Civilian Marksmanship Program, June 1995. Three M1Cs were noted with barrels dated 11/52, 5/53 and 6/53, indicating that these rifles continued to be rebuilt.
2 The base and rings were originally numbered to each rifle but none of the 100 DCM M1Cs were matching. Receiver serial number were painted in white by hand on the scope using the last 4 digits. Most base and clamp serial numbers were 6 or more digits.

Table B-3 M1D Sniper Rifle Identifying Characteristics	
Manufacturer	Springfield, Winchester, International Harvester, Harrington & Richardson
Receiver	Any manufacturer
Serial Number Range	Any above 1,000,000
Barrel Date	1952-1953 (1)
Telescopic Sight/Magnification	M84/2.2X
Base	Attached to barrel, not marked
Clamps or Rings	Not marked
Stock Cartouche	Original Springfield inspector's cartouches may be present, plus a possible rebuild cartouche— i.e., S.A./B.— under cheek pad
Cheek Pad	Leather, undated and marked "MRT," dated or undated, or unmarked

197

The M1 Garand

Table B-3 cont. M1D Sniper Rifle Identifying Characteristics	
Flash Hider	M2 Flash Hider to 1954, T37 pronged flash hider after

1 Barrels with later dates will be observed on M1Ds built, or rebuilt, after 1953.

Table B-4 Specifications U.S. Marine Corps 1952 Sniper Rifle	
Specifications	Same as M1C
Telescopic Sight	Stith-Kollmorgen 4X Fixed Focus
Base	Griffin & Howe modified, not serial numbered to the rifle
Stock Cartouche	Original S.A./G.A.W., S.A./N.F.R. cartouche may be present, plus a rebuild cartouche—i.e., S.A./B.— under cheek pad
Cheek Pad	Leather, "MRT" marked plus date
Flash Hider	M2 to 1954, T37 after

Markings on Telescopic sights installed on the M1C and M1D Sniper Rifles and their magnifications.

Commercial Lyman Alaskan:

THE LYMAN GUN SIGHT CORP.
MADE IN U.S. A. MIDDLEFIELD, CONN   ALASKAN
U.S. PATENT NO. 2078858
Reticle Pattern: Post
Sunshade/Rubber eyecup
Magnification: 2.5X

Military Lyman Alaskan:

THE LYMAN GUN SIGHT CORP.
MADE IN U.S. A. MIDDLEFIELD, CONN   ALASKAN
U.S. PATENT NO. 2078858
Windage and Elevation mounts marked: 7634671
Windage and Elevation caps marked A7575180
Eyepiece marked: 7634670
Scope body marked: 7674029
Reticle Pattern: Post
Sunshade/Rubber eyecup
Magnification: 2.5X

The M1 Garand

M81

THE LYMAN GUN SIGHT CORP.
ALASKAN
MADE IN U.S. A. MIDDLEFIELD, CONN
U.S. PATENT NO. 2078858
TELESCOPE M81
SERIAL NO. XXXXX
STOCK NO. 84373
Windage and Elevation mounts marked: 7634671
Windage and Elevation caps marked: 7575180
Eyepiece marked: 7634670
Scope body marked: 7674029
Scope body marked: 7674029
Reticle Pattern: Crosshairs
Sunshade/Rubber eyecup
Magnification: 2.2X

TELESCOPE M81
SERIAL NO. XXXXX
STOCK NO. 84373
Windage and Elevation mounts marked: 7634671
Windage and Elevation caps marked: 7575180
Eyepiece marked: 7634670
Scope body marked: 7674029
Reticle Pattern: Crosshairs
Sunshade/Rubber eyecup
Magnification: 2.2X

M82

TELESCOPE M82
SERIAL NO. XXXXX
STOCK NO. 84374
(F001-0084688 if mfg'd. after 1948)
Windage and Elevation mounts marked: 7634671
Windage and Elevation caps marked: 7575180
Eyepiece marked: 7634670
Scope body marked: 7674029
Reticle Pattern: Post
Sunshade/Rubber eyecup
Magnification: 2.2X

M84, Libby-Owens-Ford

TELESCOPE
M84
SERIAL NO. XXXXX
Reticle Pattern: Post and elevation cross hair
Sunshade/Rubber eyecup
Magnification: 2.2X

199

The M1 Garand

Stith-Kollmorgen 4XD MC-1

STITH MOUNTS S.A. TEX.
4X DOUBLE
KOLLMORGEN OPTICAL CORP
BROOKLYN N.Y.
PAT. PEND.

"MC" and serial number on top or side of tube

Eyepiece Markings (Early Production)

4X Double/
STITH-KOLLMORGEN OPTICAL CORP.

Eyepiece Markings (Later Production)

"U.S."/
FSN-1240-647-1106
TELESCOPE, RIFLE, 4XD, MC-1

STITH-KOLLMORGEN OPTICAL CORP.

Mount Markings
(Early)
GRIFFIN & HOWE, INC. NEW YORK
PAT. # 1,856,549 MAY 3 1932

(Late)
FSN 1240-647-1107
MOUNT TELESCOPE
GRIFFIN AND HOWE, INC.
U.S.

Magnification: 4X
Eye Relief: 3.5 inches approximately
Field of View at 100 Yards: 30 feet
Diameter of Telescope Body: 1 inch

APPENDIX C
NATIONAL MATCH M1 GARAND RIFLES

Target matches using the current service rifle were a feature of military training throughout the 20th century and continue today. In 1903, Congress established the National Board for the Promotion of Rifle Practice (NBPRP) and the National Rifle and Pistol Matches. In 1905, Congress passed further legislation authorizing the sale, at cost, of military surplus rifles, ammunition as well as other military equipment to civilian rifle clubs. In 1916, the office of the Director, Civilian Marksmanship (DCM) was established to encourage the participation of civilian shooters in the National Matches. The intent was to reduce the costs and time associated with rifle training in time of war.

As the Model 1903 Springfield replaced the Model 1892 Krag rifle in service, interest in national match competition increased. Springfield Armory, at the direction of the Ordnance Department, developed special techniques for improving the accuracy of the '03 Springfield service rifle. After World War II, when national match competition had been resumed, Springfield Armory again developed special techniques for improving the accuracy of the M1 Garand as a competition rifle.

In 1953, eight hundred M1 Garands were selected from standard production rifles for superior accuracy and made available to qualified national match competitors. The following year, a total of 4,184 new rifles were selected and 499 older rifles were rebuilt for superior national match accuracy. Table C-1 provides an annual breakdown of new vs rebuilt rifles from 1953 through the end of production in 1963.

Table C-1 M1 Garand National Match Production 1953-1963			
Year	New Production	Rebuilt	Total Production
1953	800	0	800
1954	4,184	499	4,683
1955	3,003	314	3,317
1956	5,050	550	5,600
1957	4,184	499	4,683
1958	1,295	731	2,026

The M1 Garand

Table C-1, cont. M1 Garand National Match Production 1953-1963			
Year	New Production	Rebuilt	Total Production
1959	2,877	2,652	5,529
1960	0	8,663*	8,663
1961	0	1,410*	1,410
1962	0	4,500*	4,500
1963	0	3,639*	3,639
* Type 3 National Match configuration using high-numbered receivers			

National match shooters complained that the M1 Garand was not as accurate as the 1903A1 Springfield National Match Rifles. In 1956 a new specifications were drawn up which all M1 Garands designated as National Match rifles after 1959 would have to meet. At the same meeting, techniques and instruments were authorized to enable the M1 Garand to meet these new specifications.

National Match rifles had been largely selected before 1958 on the basis of barrels which met strict standards regarding the concentricity of lands and grooves as measured by air gauging. On these barrels, the splines were modified to hold the gas cylinder in place with a minimum of wobble. Harrington & Richardson- and LMR-marked barrels were used to build National Match rifles if they met standards.

Starting in 1958, Springfield manufactured special M1 Garand National Match barrels. The first, part number 7790134, had a rifling groove diameter of 0.3075 ± 0.0020 inch and a bore diameter of 0.2995 ± 0.002 inch. From 1961, a second barrel, part number 7790135, was also used. Its specifications called for a rifling groove diameter of 0.3075 ± 0.0010 inch and a bore diameter of 0.300 ± 0.001 inch. Both barrels were crowned with an angle of 60 degrees ± 30 minutes. The bore deviation from the centerline of either barrel was not allowed to vary more than 0 degree, 2 minutes and 23 seconds throughout its length. All were marked "NM."

The second most important aspect of "accurizing" the National Match rifle was the development and installation of new rear and front sights, see Figure C-1. Starting in 1959, new rear sight bases and components were designed and installed on National Match Garands. The threads on the windage knobs were changed to 5/16-64NS-3A and on the

202

base of the rear sight to 5/16-64NS-3B. Most of these new rear sight components were also marked "NM." Smaller apertures with diameters of 0.0520 inch and 0.0595 inch were also introduced along with the narrow 0.05-inch-wide front sight blade.

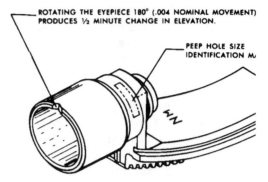

NOTCH INDICATES POSITION OF PEEP HOLE.
NOTCH AT TOP RAISES POINT OF IMPACT OF BULLET.
NOTCH AT BOTTOM LOWERS POINT OF IMPACT OF BULLET.

ROTATING THE EYEPIECE 180° (.004 NOMINAL MOVEMENT) PRODUCES ½ MINUTE CHANGE IN ELEVATION.

PEEP HOLE SIZE IDENTIFICATION M

In 1962, the sighting aperture was covered by a hood to shut out extraneous light. The hood was

Figure C-1. The M1 Garand National Match Rear Sight

0.45 inch long by 0.470 inch in diameter. The exterior of the hood was knurled, the knurl lines running fore and aft in relation to the eye. The curved ramp was marked on the top NM for National Match in sans serif letters 0.08 inch high. Refer to Figure C-1.

NOTE: Billy Pyle, the editor of *Garand Stand Report* (see Aids for Collectors), warns that many new National Match bases, knobs and hooded apertures found for sale today are new reproductions. Be careful!

The two apertures introduced the previous year with peep holes of 0.0520 and 0.0595 inch in diameter were made standard. The aperture in combination with the hood was capable of producing a 1/2 minute of angle change in elevation by turning the assembly 180 degrees. A notch was cut into the aperture hood to indicate the position of the peep hole.

Beginning also in 1963, a modified operating rod which was specially straightened and held to tighter tolerances was substituted for the standard operating rod. These were marked "NM" and with the part number, "7790722-RA or SA." "RA" indicated manufacture by Remington Arms and "SA" by Springfield Armory.

Another factor that assured the accuracy of the M1 Garand National Match rifle after 1959 was the stock. Straight-grained black walnut was selected for lack of open grain and carefully fitted to the receiver by replacing wood with a fiberglass insert. Channels were routed at the

The M1 Garand

rear top and side top of the receiver and at the rear of the trigger guard area. The bedding material was poured into these areas and allowed to harden. The receiver was handfitted by slowly removing the bedding material until the trigger guard started to bind when closed 3/4 inch from lockup. The result was a secure clamp between stock and receiver with no side-to-side, up-and-down or fore-and-aft movement. The barrel channel was further routed, if necessary, to assure that at no point did the barrel touch the wood. See the notes in Figure C-2.

"Trigger pull" was adjusted to between 4 and 6 1/2 pounds, without creep. All rubbing surfaces were carefully polished to reduce friction. Varying degrees of workmanship will be found throughout the period of National Match M1 Garand production.

The authors developed the following guide to assist you in identifying a National Match M1 Garand according to the period in which it was built. The Types and Variations are not official descriptions but our own classifications. We welcome any comments or corrections.

Table C-2 National Match M1 Garand Criteria	
Type 1A	Original 800 M1 Garands ordered and produced in 1953. Barrels marked "NM" and dated 1952. Can only be positively identified through DCM papers
Type 1B	New and rebuilt M1 Garands. Minor tune-up of trigger assemblies. Barrels marked "NM." Built from 1953-56. Can only be positively identified through DCM papers.
Type 2	Rebuilt M1 Garands in 1957-1958. Minor tune-up for accuracy, barrels marked "NM." May also show a small six-pointed star at the muzzle indicating the use of the "star gauge." Rear sight may be marked "SA." Barrels dated 1955 and 1956.

The M1 Garand

Table C-2, cont. National Match M1 Garand Criteria	
Type 3A	Rebuilt M1 Garands in 1959. Special "NM"-marked rear sight bases, air-gauged barrels, barrels marked "NM," smaller-diameter apertures (0.0520 and 0.0595 inch) and 0.05 inch wide front sight.
Type 3B	Rebuilt M1 Garands in 1960-61. Special "NM"-marked rear sight bases, air-gauged barrels, barrels marked "NM" and dated 1960-61, glass-bedded stocks, smaller diameter apertures (0.0520 and 0.0595 inch) and 0.05 inch wide front sight.
Type 3C	Rebuilt M1 Garands in 1962. Special "NM"-marked rear sight bases, air-gauged barrels, barrels marked "NM" and dated 1962-67, glass-bedded stocks, smaller-diameter apertures (0.0520 and 0.0595 inch), and hooded rear sight aperture
Type 3D	Rebuilt M1 Garand in 1963-to End of Use. Special "NM"-marked rear sight bases, air-gauged barrels, barrels marked "NM" and dated 1963 through 1967, glass-bedded stocks, hooded rear sight aperture, smaller-diameter apertures (0.0520 and 0.0595 inch), and new operating rods marked "NM"

The M1 Garand reigned supreme in the National Matches until the mid-1960s when it was superseded by its offspring, the M14.

NOTE: National Match M1 Garands "evolved" over a ten-year period. Not all can be fitted neatly into the categories listed above. The only way to be certain that an M1 Garand is a true Springfield Armory-made

The M1 Garand

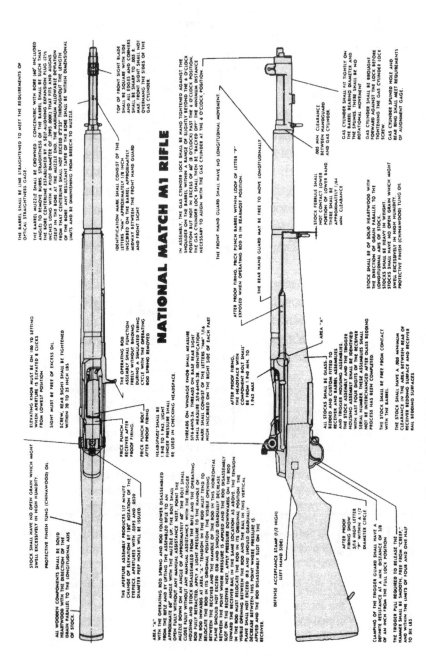

Figure C-2. M1 Garand National Match Characteristics

The M1 Garand

National Match rifle is by examining the documents that accompanied the rifle from the Director, Civilian Marksmanship Program. If this documentation is not available for a particular rifle, you may write to the Director, Rock Island Arsenal, Rock Island, IL, and request a copy of Forms DA 450-22-A, DD 149 or DD 1348.

NOTE: The National Board for the Promotion of Rifle Practice (NBPRP) was established in 1903 as an advisory board to the Secretary of the Army to promote firearms training and marksmanship among young civilians. The hope was that they would produce a pool of young men already trained in the use of firearms in time of war. The NBPRP established the Director of Civilian Marksmanship (DCM) in 1916 to provide arms, ammunition, and, in cooperation with the National Rifle Association, firearms training. Over the years, the program was broadened to include children of school age as a way of teaching discipline, knowledge, and respect regarding firearms. In past years, as elitist Congressional elements gained position in the federal government and pushed a gun-control agenda, the DCM also came under attack. In 1996, they succeeded in severing the DCM from government support. The National Defense Authorization Act for Fiscal Year 1996 (Title XVI) created the Corporation for the Promotion of Rifle Practice and Firearms Safety, Inc., as a tax-exempt, not-for-profit organization to administer the CMP. The Act specifically forbids the use of federally appropriated funds to conduct CMP Operations and therefore, the CMP must generate its own operating expenses, which it does through authorized sales of surplus .22- and .30-caliber rifles, ammunition and spare parts to qualified individuals and affiliated clubs and associations. The CMP continues to support and encourage clubs and state associations, and emphasizes strong junior programs.

The authors urge all members of the firearms collecting and shooting public to be aware that the CMP continues under attack from elitist politicians as well as anti-Second Amendment factions from all walks of life. You can best safeguard the CMP and allow it to continue its over 100-year-old mission by joining the National Rifle Association so that you can be made aware of future threats. And you can support the CMP by participating in its activities and purchasing rifles, ammunition and spare parts from its stocks. Address correspondence to Civilian Marksmanship Program, P.O. Box 576, Port Clinton, Ohio 43452. The CMP's Web site is http://www.odcmp.com.

APPENDIX D
U.S. NAVY AND OTHER 7.62 X 51 MM
NATO M1 GARANDS

Even at the height of the Cold War, military budgets were under intense scrutiny and there was little slack to be found. In 1957, the U.S. Navy had on hand sufficient M1 Garand rifles in .30-06 caliber for their needs. But the U.S. Army—and the rest of NATO—had switched to the 7.62 mm NATO cartridge which was essentially a shortened .30-06 cartridge with very similar ballistics. It became the policy of the United States government to conform to the NATO policy of standardizing weapons and parts which the U.S. Army and Air Force had worked so hard to implement. The Navy had no choice but to switch to the new cartridge.

To do so without the extensive fiscal outlay for the new M14 rifles the U.S. Army had recently adopted, the Navy asked the H.P. White Laboratories to develop a steel insert or bushing that could be inserted into the chamber of the .30-06 Garand so that it would accept the shorter 7.62 mm cartridge.

To function properly, the gas port was reamed to a slightly larger diameter to allow more gas into the barrel from the less-powerful 7.62 mm NATO cartridge. The bushing was inserted into the chamber ahead of a 7.62 mm cartridge which was then fired. This wedged the bushing into the chamber and the M1 Garand could be fired from then on with the new NATO cartridge. A plastic spacer was added to the clip well to position the cartridge properly and to avoid locking in a clip of .30-06 ammunition, which, of course, could not chamber due to the longer length of the cartridge.

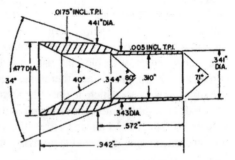

Figure D-1. .308 Bushing to convert the .30-06 M1 Garand to 7.62 x 51 mm NATO

The bushing was designated "Bushing, 7.62 mm, BUWEPS Dwg. 2256892, Steel Leadloy A," see Figure D-1. The left side of all receivers so modified was stamped "7.62 NATO" and the barrel was

The M1 Garand

marked "H&R G 7.62 NATO" under the operating rod and beneath the original barrel date. The rifle was designated "U.S. Rifle, Navy Mk. 2, Mod 0, Caliber 7.62 mm." The majority of these rifles were modified by Harrington & Richardson Arms.

Because the bushings had a tendency to "work" loose and be extracted with an empty case, the Navy acquired 30,000 new M1 Garand barrels manufactured by the Springfield Armory in 1965-66, chambered for the 7.62 mm NATO cartridge. These were marked "SA 11686514 -XX (Month)-XX (Year) - MO61." Those rifles that had the bushing inserted were recalled and the new barrels were installed. These were designated U.S. Rifle, Navy Mk. 2, Mod 1, Caliber 7.62 mm, and can be distinguished by the marking on the receiver, "7.62 mm NATO." Many of these venerable M1 Garands are still to be found in Naval armories today. The Mk. 2, Mod 0 rifles with the bushing were converted to the Mk. 2, Mod 1 by American Machine & Foundry and so, almost none have survived.

Both modifications of the Mk. 2 rifle were built primarily on postwar M1 Garands manufactured after production resumed in the 1950s. As such, they were equipped with newly manufactured stocks, some walnut, but the majority were birch. Most lack arsenal markings or proof marks of any kind.

The U.S. Navy built two variations of the U.S. Rifle, Navy Mk. 2, Mod 1, Caliber 7.62 mm as match rifles, designated U.S. Rifle, Navy Mk. 2, Match Grade A, Caliber 7.62 mm and U.S. Rifle, Navy

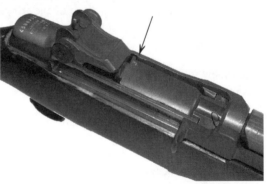

Figure D-2. U.S. Rifle, Navy Mk. 2, Mod 1, Caliber 7.62 mm Match Grade B Garand.

Mk. 2, Match Grade B, Caliber 7.62 mm, see Figure D-2. Those U.S. Navy Mk. 2, Mod 1s which were rendered non-operational were designated U.S. Navy Mk. 6, Dummy Drill Rifle.

The Navy match-grade rifles were built by U.S. Navy armorers at the Naval Surface Warfare Center, Crane Division, Crane, IN, in the early 1980s. The Grade A rifles had fiberglass-bedded receivers

The M1 Garand

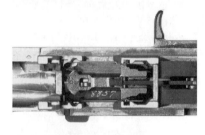

Figure D-3. Placement of serial number markings on U.S. Navy Mk. 2, Mod. Grade A and B match rifles.

and were furnished with National Match sights. The Grade B rifles also had fiberglass-bedded stocks but retained the standard battle sights. Both the Grade A and Grade B stocks were birch, although in some instances existing or replacement walnut stocks were used. The stocks are normally without markings except as noted in the next paragraph.

Both grades were refitted with National Match operating rods. Grade A rifles were stamped "A" in a box on the bottom of the pistol grip and Grade B rifles were stamped "B." The last four digits of the receiver serial number were stamped or etched with an electric pencil (Figure D-3) on the inside of the trigger guard housing floor plate, the bottom of the bolt (with the last two digits of the serial number etched on the top of the bolt, arrow in Figure D-2) and stamped on the right upper side of the stock just above the inletting for the trigger.

A word about the stocks. NSWC gunsmiths were more concerned with how well their rifles shot rather than their appearance. A good many of the Grade A and B rifles will have mismatched birch and walnut stocks and handguards. The collector should not be put off by their appearance. They shot as well as their Army National Match counterparts.

Many Mk. 2, Mod 1, Grade A and B Match rifles have been awarded over the past few years to Naval personnel participating in Navy rifle matches. The majority of such awards involved the Grade B rifles.

The M1 Garands in 7.62 mm NATO were also used by other allied and friendly nations—Denmark and Pakistan, to name but two, see Table D-1 for a complete listing. Markings on these M1 Garands will vary from country to country. For instance, the Danish M1 Garands were converted by Beretta in Italy. Many American parts were replaced

The M1 Garand

if worn or unserviceable with parts manufactured by Beretta, which are marked "PB." See Appendix F for additional details. Pakistani M1s were converted with the H.P. White Laboratories bushing and the plastic spacer in the clip well. Most of the rifles shipped to Pakistan were of post-World War II manufacture. Their barrels were marked "7.62 mm NATO MII." These letters and numbers were stamped by hand.

Table D-1 M1 Garand Usage by Country		
Austria	Haiti	Panama
Colombia	Honduras	Paraguay
Cuba	Iran	Philippines
Denmark	Iraq	South Korea
El Salvador	Italy	South Vietnam
Ethiopia	Japan	Thailand
France (WW II)	Liberia	United Kingdom
Germany (West)	Netherlands	Uruguay
Greece	Pakistan	USA

APPENDIX E
BRITISH M1 GARANDS

After the German capture of the Channel ports in late May 1940, the Allies organized Operation Dynamo to evacuate the British Expeditionary Force from Dunkirk. Between May 26 to June 4, 1940, a total of 338,226 British, French and Belgian troops were rescued from the beaches surrounding the small French port. The BEF lost virtually all of its heavy equipment and most of its small arms. The United States, at the direction of President Franklin D. Roosevelt under the Lend-Lease Act of February 1941, shipped 38,001 M1 Garand rifles to Great Britain. Because of the shortage of .30-06 caliber ammunition which was not manufactured in Great Britain, and the difficulties in training troops, the M1 Garands were issued in small quantities only to the Home Guard.

The Home Guard was a reserve military organization made up of volunteers not otherwise liable to military service, somewhat akin to the State-chartered militia units in the United States. They guarded coastal areas, vital tactical points and military production facilities and later undertook antiaircraft and other such duties. After World War II ended, the M1 Garands were stored until the mid- to late 1950s when they were sold on the international arms market. A number of these M1 Garands were thus returned to the United States, where they are often encountered by collectors. Recently, dismantled British M1 rifles minus their receivers have been imported as spare parts.

The British M1 Garand is relatively easy to identify. Most M1s sent to Great Britain as lend-lease material were manufactured before mid-summer 1942. Many were painted with a red stripe approximately 1.5 inches wide around the upper band to indicate .30-06 caliber. Some, but not all stocks and handguards had the "broad arrow" of the British War Department stamped into the wood. And some, but not all hand-guards were marked "3006" in black paint.

These M1 Garands *were not* proof marked by the British War Department during World War II. The proof marks observed on metal parts of many "British" M1 Garands are *commercial* proof markings required by the British proof laws of 1925 or 1955 and have nothing to do with British *military* markings. Therefore, the fact that an M1 Garand has British proof marks does not necessarily make it one of the M1 Garands sent to Great Britain during World War II. M1 Garands given as aid to other countries which were transferred through, or stored in

The M1 Garand

or sold from Great Britain would have been subjected to British proof laws and so marked.

As an example, two M1 Garands have been observed with British proof marks, one manufactured by Harrington and Richardson and the other a later World War II Springfield with a replaced barrel dated 1964. The barrels on both M1s showed the third style of British proof marks listed below. The following are the three most common styles of British commercial proof marks observed.

Commercial British Proof Marks

1) The initials "BNP" for British Nitro Proof were stamped on the bolt lug and the receiver ring. As these parts were hardened during manufacture, the stamp is usually indistinct and appears as a dent or flaw. This marking, shown here, was not applied during World War II, but was required by the British Proof Laws of 1955 and was applied before the rifles were resold on the international market.

2) Three types of barrel markings have been observed:

a) on top of the barrel, in front of the front handguard

 .30   2.494"
18   TONS PER □"

b) on the right side of the barrel, under the operating slide

 .30/06 2.494" 18 TONSPER □"

c) on the right side of the barrel, under the operating slide, will show either the "crown/GP" or the "Arm and Sword" followed by

 .30/06 2.494" 18 TONSPER □"

213

The M1 Garand

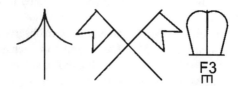

BRITISH MILITARY PROOF MARKS

British military proof marks of the World War II period included the Broad Arrow (left) and crossed swallowtail pennants (center). If the firearm was inspected at Enfield Lock, where all firearms used by the British Army were accepted, they would also have one or more marks in the form of a Crown over a letter/number over the letter "E" for Enfield, either upright or lying on its side (right). The authors have never observed an M1 Garand with these markings.

The collector should keep in mind that in the post-World War II years, a great many M1 Garands from various sources were sold and resold on the international arms market. In the post-World War II years, Great Britain was a center for the resale of surplus military equipment and many international arms dealers stored M1 Garands and other weaponry in Great Britain. If resold, either in Great Britain or outside the country, British firearms laws required that they be proof-tested and marked. Thus M1 Garands purchased from one country for sale in another would show British commercial proof marks if the resale took place from Great Britain, regardless of whether or not they had been used by the British military. Likewise, an M1 Garand sold in Great Britain to circa 1991, when the sale of all semiautomatic weapons ended by law, would also show these proof marks.

APPENDIX F
DANISH M1 GARANDS

On April 9, 1940, Nazi German forces attacked and occupied Norway and Denmark (Operation *Weserübung*) to secure access to Swedish iron ore deposits which were shipped through the Norwegian port of Narvik. A secondary objective was to gain additional air and naval bases on the North Sea and North Atlantic.

The Occupation of Denmark was relatively benign. The Germans considered the Danes to be fellow Aryans although for the most part, the feeling was not reciprocated. King Christian X refused to either leave the country or abdicate, preferring instead a policy of limited collaboration to protect the Danish people. The government was instrumental in smuggling almost all Danish Jews to safety in Norway and the King himself referred to Danish Jews only as Danish citizens. A story, possibly apocryphal, had the King wearing the yellow Star of David as a protest.

Almost as soon as the Nazi Occupation began, Danish resistance groups sprang into being. They became so effective that on August 26, 1943, the Nazis declared martial law in Denmark and disarmed the Army and police, confiscating their Krag-Jørgensen M1889/10 rifles and M1889/24 carbines.

As the resistance hardened, weapons became more and more of a problem. In addition to hunting and sporting rifles and handguns and the few weapons captured from the Nazis, the Resistance leaders persuaded the British to provide Enfield rifles, grenades and other explosives through the auspices of the Special Operations Executive (SOE).

When the war ended in early May 1945, members of the Danish Resistance rounded up the demoralized German military and security forces for internment. Within days, the Danish military forces were reconstituted. Their armament consisted of a hodgepodge of weapons including some prewar Danish arms that were recovered, British Enfields and .380 Enfield Mark 2 revolvers furnished by SOE, and Mauser bolt-action rifles taken from Nazi German forces. Sweden also provided a large number of their m/96-38 and m/38 bolt-action rifles as well and the United States, a small number of M1 Garands and M1 Carbines.

At the time that Denmark became a part of NATO, the Danish government approached the U.S. government for weapons for their small but efficient army. The U.S. agreed and shipped 20,000 M1 Garands to Denmark on loan. These rifles could not be provided under the provisions of the Lend-Lease Act of 1941 as the country was occupied by

The M1 Garand

the Nazis from April 1940 to May 1945. The following year, Denmark purchased between 30,000 and 40,000 additional M1 Garands. In Danish service, they were designated the Gevaer Model 1950 (G M/50).

Because the M1 Garand was a NATO-standard weapon, spare parts had to be manufactured to NATO specification which were, in effect, the same specifications established by the U.S. Army Ordnance Department. In 1952, the Italian firearms-manufacturing firm of Beretta was selected as the European manufacturer of new M1 Garands and spare parts. Machinery used by Winchester during World War II to manufacture the M1 Garand was shipped to Beretta. Breda, a state-owned arms manufacturer, also was provided with contracts for complete M1 Garand rifles and spare parts.

As the American M1 Garands began to wear out, Denmark bought an additional 13,966 M1 rifles from both Beretta and Breda as well as an extensive supply of spare parts. Starting in 1962, the Danes manufactured barrels for the M1 Garand, as well as stocks, slings, bayonets and ammunition. The M1 Garand remained in service with the Danish military through the early 1990s until replaced by the West German G3A5 select-fire rifles which were acquired on lease. It should be noted that most Danish M1 Garands were manufactured originally at the Springfield National Armory or by Winchester and will be of World War II vintage. The sale of M1 Garands to Denmark was completed before manufacturing began at International Harvester and Harrington & Richardson. In addition to the American M1 Garands, Denmark also acquired a quantity of Beretta- and Breda-manufactured M1 Garands.

In the late 1990s, Denmark began to return the 20,000 borrowed M1 Garands to the United States. Both complete rifles and spare parts were made available to civilian shooters and collectors through the Civilian Marksmanship Program. Other M1 Garands, presumably from the 30,000 to 40,000 M1 Garands purchased in 1951, were sold to the Danish export company, Topmark, who resold them to various export-import groups in the United States. Some found their way into the United States before the Clinton Administration's executive order prohibiting the importation of semiautomatic military firearms. Many of these remaining M1 Garands were disassembled and entered the United States as "parts kits."

A survey of thirty-one Danish M1 Garands was conducted for North Cape Publications, Inc., by Adam Fatore of J.N.J. Arms, Ltd., Dyer, IN. They were randomly selected from among the several hundred Danish M1 Garands which that company imported.

The M1 Garand

OVERALL

The serial number range in this survey of thirty-one randomly selected M1 Garands covers virtually the entire range of World War II production. The earliest date of receiver manufacture was October 1940 and the latest was November 1944. Two of the rifles were manufactured in 1940, three in 1941, five in 1942, seventeen in 1943 and four in 1944. This appears to be roughly consistent not only with the accelerating wartime production but also with the speed with which the rifles were transported to the European Theater of Operations. Keep in mind that combat rifles have a relatively short life span before they are returned for repair and refurbishing, or for disassembly for spare parts. Thus many, if not most rifles issued before the end of 1944 would have been rebuilt and while later 1944- and 1945-manufactured rifles would have still been in service at the end of the war.

Although both Springfield and Winchester M1 Garands have been observed with Danish markings, this selection included only Springfield production. Replacement parts included both Springfield and Winchester production seemingly in proportion to their original manufacture. And while some replacement parts were manufactured by International Harvester and Harrington & Richardson, there were no complete rifles by these manufacturers, nor should there have been as M1 Garand shipments to Denmark had been completed by the time those two factories began manufacture. It should be noted that many of the M1 Garands manufactured in 1942 and 1943 that have been returned and sold through the CMP have many replacement parts manufactured by Beretta (PB) and Breda (BMB).

NOTE: The initials "BMR" and "BMP" have also been observed on Breda-manufactured parts.

BARRELS

Of the thirty-one rifles in the survey, only three retained their original barrels (barrel dates matching receiver serial numbers). The rest, as might be expected, had replacement barrels dated from May 1942 to October 1966. Replacement barrels were, in order of frequency, Springfield, Marlin, Breda and two were unmarked and therefore of unknown origin. Seventeen of the barrels were of Springfield manufacture, eleven were made by Marlin, one was manufactured by Breda and the remaining two, as noted above, were unmarked.

The M1 Garand

  Fourteen of the seventeen Springfield barrels had no Danish markings but three more did. One showed only the Navy anchor and "M." Two barrels also had the complete Danish barrel marking described below.

  Ten of the eleven Marlin barrels carried the complete Danish markings but one did not. Two of the Marlin barrels also were marked with the Danish "M," possibly indicating Naval (Marine) service.

  Two of the barrels were marked REP 43 and PSA, respectively. The meaning of these designations is not known to the authors.

REAR SIGHTS

Twenty-three rifles retained U.S.-manufactured rear sights, both Types 2/3 and Type 4. Three had replacement rear sight components manufactured by Beretta and one, sight components from Breda. Interestingly enough, seven rear sights had Harrington & Richardson (3) and International Harvester (4) rear sight components, suggesting delivery of additional spare parts from the U.S. after the mid-1950s.

STOCKS

Only three of the thirty-one rifles retained their original American walnut stocks complete with cartouches. Eleven others were American walnut without cartouches. The remaining seventeen had replaced stocks made of beech, probably of Danish or Italian origin. All of these lacked the "P" firing proofs. The remaining American replacement stocks all had a plug drilled out on the bottom of the pistol grip for a unit marking disk near the "P" firing proof. Twenty-three of the thirty-one stocks had deeply stamped serial numbers on the bottom of the buttstock.

HANDGUARDS

Ten rifle handguards were replaced with Danish-made handguards. These were identified by a paper sticker with the letters, "HTK."

TRIGGER GUARD HOUSINGS

Three types of trigger guard housings were encountered in the thirty-one rifles surveyed. Twenty-one were of Springfield manufacture (only five had part numbers consistent with receiver serial numbers), nine were manufactured by Winchester and one by Beretta. Trigger guard assemblies were not disassembled to identify each part as it was assumed that after forty years of service, few parts would be original.

The M1 Garand

OPERATING RODS
Twenty-six operating rods were manufactured by Springfield, three by Winchester and two by Breda (BMB; may also show BMR, BMP) on the thirty-one rifles surveyed.

BOLTS
Twenty-five bolts were manufactured by Springfield but none in the survey were by Winchester. Three were manufactured by Breda (BMB), two by Beretta (PB), and one by an unknown manufacturer was unmarked.

DANISH M1D SNIPER RIFLE
One of the authors had occasion to examine a Danish M1D obtained through the Civilian Marksmanship Program. The telescopic sight was the standard M84 but was marked with the Danish Crown property mark and the initials "FKF" signifying Danish military service. An additional serial or part number, "305292," had also been stamped in front of the eyepiece. The mount was marked with an "M" in a semicircle. The stock had been replaced and did not show either an American or Danish cartouche.

DANISH MARKINGS
Perhaps most important to the identification of Danish M1 Garands is the barrel marking. The majority of rifles surveyed showed the following barrel marking:

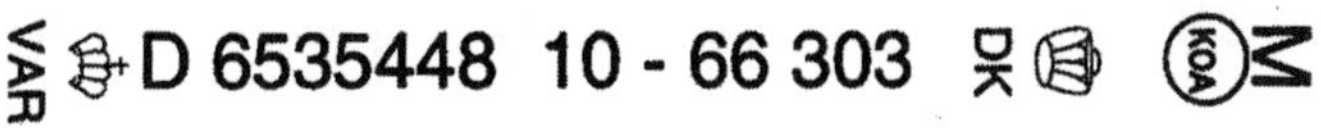

VAR ⌐D 6535448 10 - 66 303 DK ⊞ Ⓜ

Figure F-1. Danish Barrel Marking

The "Crown/DK" marking signifies that the barrel has been proof-tested. The "Crown/VAR" marking indicates that the rifle was inspected, repaired or refurbished at the Haerens Vaabenarsenalet (Army Weapons Arsenal). This arsenal was closed in 1970. Occasionally, an older version of the same mark, "Crown/VA," is seen. The seven-digit number above the "Crown/VAR" is the part number, followed by the month and year.

Barrel markings found on Beretta- and Breda-manufactured replacement barrels are shown immediately below, as well as bolts and operating rods. Also shown is a stock cartouche observed on a beech replacement stock. The initials are probably those of a Danish inspector or facility.

The M1 Garand

Figure F-2. Manufacturer (Breda) and Part Number on top of barrel over chamber.

Figure F-3. Date of installation (right side of barrel) visible through the operating rod slot.

Figure F-4. Stock cartouche observed.

Figure F-5. Beretta stock mark.

The following marks will be found on stocks and accessories:
Other stock marks:
An anchor signifies the Danish Naval service
HTK — Haerens Tekniske Korps (Army Technical Corps)
FKF — Forsvarets Krigsmaterial Forvaltning (Defense War Material Administration)
HMAK — Haerens Material Kommando (Army Material Command)

Receivers of Danish M1 Garands will carry Springfield Armory or Winchester World War II period markings. If a receiver has been replaced, or the rifle was manufactured for the Danish military, it will

Figures F-6 and 7. Beretta receiver markings.

Top   Left Side

The M1 Garand

Figures F-8 and 9. Breda receiver markings.

carry Beretta or Breda markings. The initials of Italian manufacturers will also be found on replacement parts: PB — Beretta; BMR — Breda (also BMB and BMP).

Figures F-10 Bolt manufactured by Breda.

Fig F-11. Operating rod manufactured by Breda.

The M1 Garand

BAYONETS

The Danes used the 10-inch Bayonet, M1, many of them remanufactured from the Springfield Model 1905 knife bayonet. They also manufactured new bayonets to the same pattern. These are marked with the initials "FKF" and the Danish crown.

Danish-manufactured scabbards are made of fiberglass with a simulated wood grain. The steel throats are marked with either the initials "FKF" or "HTK" and the Danish crown.

Figures F-12 and 13. Danish M1 Garand bayonet scabbards: (left) issued by Haerens Tekniske Korps; (right) issued by Forsvarets Krigsmaterial Forvaltning.

222

APPENDIX G
DISASSEMBLY, ASSEMBLY, CLEANING AND
MAINTENANCE OF THE M1 RIFLE

The M1 rifle receiver/barrel is held in the stock by the clamping action of the trigger housing. If you wish to disassemble the rifle, use the following procedure.

NOTE: Draw back on the operating slide handle and look into the breech to make certain that the rifle is unloaded. If it is not, unload it. Never, ever try to disassemble a loaded firearm of any kind. Also, when disassembling any firearm where there are springs under tension, the authors and publisher strongly recommend that you wear safety glasses.

The trigger guard has two studs, one on each side, which mesh with slots in the receiver to hold the trigger-housing group and the receiver together. The trigger guard pivots at the front and latches at the rear. The rifle is disassembled by unlatching the trigger guard (pull back and up) and swinging it down and forward to disengage the two lugs from their slots in the receiver. To do so, pull the trigger guard out, then turn the rifle upside down and rest the muzzle on a flat surface and tap gently to separate the stock. No further disassembly is needed for cleaning and oiling.

To **reassemble the stock to the barrel/receiver**, slide the flange at the front of the stock into the lower band and pivot the stock down over the receiver. Unlatch and open the trigger guard; keeping the base of the trigger housing level, move it straight down into the receiver so that the locking lugs on the trigger guard enter their slots in the receiver. Close and latch the trigger guard.

To test the assembly, pull the operating rod all the way to the rear. The bolt should remain open. Close the bolt by placing the heel of your right hand against the operating rod handle to control it. Use the thumb of your left hand to depress the follower and release the bolt. Take up the operating rod pressure with the heel of your right hand and ease the bolt forward while withdrawing your left thumb. This procedure avoids the infamous and painful "M1 Garand Thumb" which occurs when the bolt snaps forward, pinching your thumb against the front of the receiver. Push the safety to the locked position. Pull the trigger. The hammer should not fall. Push the safety forward. Pull the trigger. The hammer should fall.

If the rifle is to be disassembled further, place the parts on a clean, flat surface in the order in which they were removed. This will make it easier to reassemble the rifle and its components.

BARREL/RECEIVER DISASSEMBLY
Lay the barrel and receiver group on the table or bench with the sights down and the muzzle to the left. To **remove the operating rod spring and follower rod,**

The M1 Garand

grasp the follower rod with the thumb and forefinger of the left hand and pull back toward the muzzle to disengage the claws of the follower rod from the front studs of the follower arm.

To **replace the operating rod spring and the follower rod**, place the end of the follower rod into the end of the operating rod spring. Hold the follower rod with your left hand and pull it toward the muzzle. Then fit its claw over the front studs of the follower arm, being sure that the hump, or rounded curve, fits through the slotted space between the arms of the operating rod catch assembly. When the rifle is right side up, the curve of the hump should be down.

To **remove the bullet guide, follower arm, follower, and operating rod catch assembly**, push out the pin holding them in the receiver, then remove and separate the parts. Do not separate the accelerator from the operating rod catch assembly as the accelerator pin is riveted in place.

To **replace the bullet guide, follower, follower rod, and operating rod catch assembly**, place the barrel and receiver group sights down, muzzle to the left. Insert the shoulders of the bullet guide in their recesses in the receiver. Raise the bullet guide slightly to replace the operating rod catch, making sure that the rear arm is underneath and engaged with the front stud of the clip latch. Insert the studded end of the follower arm through the slot in the bullet guide and into the guide grooves on the follower. The narrow end of the follower should be to the rear. Line up the holes and insert the follower arm pin through the side of the receiver nearest you, seating it all the way.

To **remove the operating rod**, turn the barrel/receiver so that the sights are up and the muzzle is to the left. Draw the operating rod handle to the rear until the rear edge of the handle is in a line with the front edge of the windage knob on the rear sight. The guide lug should be in the dismount notch on the receiver. Place your left hand over the open receiver, fingers curled under the operating rod, thumb against the inside of the hump, and grasp the operating rod handle with the thumb and forefinger of the right hand. Lift up with the right hand, at the same time pressing outward with the left thumb, and disengage the operating rod.

To **replace the operating rod**, hold the barrel and receiver group with sights down, muzzle to the left; insert the piston 3/8 inch into the gas cylinder and place the operating rod over the right side of the receiver. Turn the barrel and receiver group so that the sights are up. Place the camming recess in the hump of the operating rod over the operating lug of the bolt. Pull the rod to the rear until the rear of the handle is just behind the center of the dismount notch. The guide lug is now in the notch. Seat the rod by pressing downward and inward. Run the bolt all the way forward.

Remove the bolt by pushing it to the rear after removing the operating rod. Then grasp the bolt lug with the right hand and slide the bolt from rear to front with an upward and outward rotary motion to twist it clear of the receiver. Do this carefully to avoid scratching the finish.

The **bolt can be disassembled** by holding it in the left hand with the face of the bolt up and the operating lug to the right. Place your little finger under

The M1 Garand

the firing pin tang and your thumb over the ejector. The ejector spring is under compression and will fly out if you don't. Wear safety glasses. Insert a screwdriver between the extractor and the lower cartridge flange and pry the extractor up and out of its seat. Now release thumb pressure carefully and remove the ejector and spring.

To **reassemble the bolt**, insert the firing pin with its tang in the slot, and ejector and ejector spring. Hold the bolt with the top up and the bolt lug to your right. Set the stud of the extractor into its hole in the bolt without forcing it against the ejector spring. Place the drift of the combination tool in the left groove of the bolt, with the ejector cut in the face of the tool against the front edge of the ejector. Press toward the bolt face with the combination tool so that you are compressing the ejector spring and aligning the ejector, and at the same time push down on the extractor with the thumb of the left hand until the extractor pops into place.

If you don't have the combination tool, you can use the head of an empty cartridge to push in the ejector. Stand the bolt upright and hold it steady with your right hand. Use your left hand to push in the ejector with the empty cartridge. The extractor is forced into place with the right thumb.

To **remove the extractor while the bolt remains in the rifle**, use the M3 combination tool with the wire brush attached or the M10 tool. Retract the bolt and insert the wire brush of the combination tool, or the M10 tool, into the chamber, turned so that the lug is to the right and will be under the extractor when the bolt is closed. Push the tool forward until its shoulder bears against the breech end of the barrel. Allow the bolt to close slowly. Force the operating rod forward to compress the ejector spring, and hold the bolt forward to keep the ejector pushed back; lift the handle of the combination tool so that its lug raises the extractor out of its seat and out of engagement with the ejector.

Retract the bolt slowly and remove the extractor spring plunger assembly and the ejector assembly. The firing pin can then be withdrawn from the rear of the bolt.

To **reinstall while the bolt is the rifle**: Place the ejector and ejector spring, the firing pin, the extractor spring and plunger, and the extractor in the bolt. With the M10 tool or the brush of the combination tool in the chamber and the handle of the tool down as far as it will go, line up the notches in the firing pin and ejector, and force the operating rod forward, compressing the ejector spring. While holding the ejector spring compressed, push the extractor down to its seat.

To **replace the bolt**, hold the operating lug of the bolt in the right hand and place the base of the bolt on the bridge. Rotate the bolt to allow the tang of the firing pin to clear the bridge; seat the left locking lug in its guide groove, the right locking lug on its bearing, and slide the bolt to the rear.

To **disassemble and reassemble the clip latch**, press down on the thumb piece with the left index finger, and with the point of a bullet or the drift of the combination tool, push out the clip latch pin toward the muzzle. To reassemble, replace the clip latch with the clip latch spring in its seat, and depress

225

The M1 Garand

the thumb piece. Replace the clip latch pin. Make certain that the head of the pin seats completely.

To **remove the gas cylinder from the barrel**, unscrew the gas cylinder lock screw with the combination tool. Unscrew and remove the gas cylinder lock which is threaded onto the end of the barrel with a right-hand thread. Place the right thumb over the muzzle of the gun, grasp the rear of the front sight with the outside of the forefinger and squeeze the thumb and forefinger together, drawing the gas cylinder toward the muzzle. If this still does not do it, tap gently on the bayonet stud only until the gas cylinder loosens and moves forward.

On some rifles, the front sight stud was cut through so that the gas cylinder could be clamped tighter onto the barrel by the front sight screw. Loosen the front sight screw first with 3/16 inch hex wrench before removing the gas cylinder. Replace by reversing the procedure.

To **remove the front handguard**, slide it forward after the gas cylinder has been removed. Reverse to replace.

To **remove the rear handguard**, it is not necessary to remove the lower band. In fact, the lower band should not be removed except to be replaced. The metal clip at the rear of the handguard has a small hole in the "clip end" which fits into grooves in the barrel. Insert a small punch, or the blade of a small screwdriver and carefully pry the clips out of their slots on either side. Then lift the rear handguard from the back and wriggle it free from the flange on the lower band. **Replace the rear handguard** by sliding the front end of the handguard into the flange in the lower band, then push down on the rear of the handguard until the clip on the right side snaps into place.

DISASSEMBLY AND ASSEMBLY OF THE TRIGGER ASSEMBLY

To **remove the hammer**, drift out and remove the hammer pin toward the right side. Rotate the hammer to the rear and remove it. Open the trigger guard. Drift out the safety stud and remove the safety.

To **remove the trigger guard**, grasp the rear of the trigger guard with the right hand, swing it down and draw it to the rear until the holes in the wings are aligned with the safety stud hole. At this point the hammer stop will clear the base. Swing the trigger guard to the right and upward, removing it. You may have to vary the position slightly to wriggle it free.

To **dismount the clip ejector**, place the trigger housing on the table open side down and drift out the clip ejector through the dismount hole (the bevel hole on the left just above the trigger opening).

To **reassemble the trigger assembly**, with the right hand grasp the rear of the trigger housing, hold the open side up, the projecting base to the left. Insert the loop of the clip ejector through the slot in the vertical face, and lay it on top of the clip ejector stud. Hold the loop on the stud loosely with the right thumb. Place the left forefinger under the tang of the clip ejector, seat the tang in the notch at the top of the slot in the vertical face and hold it there firmly. Place the left thumb over the long arm of the clip ejector near the inside of the arm and the

226

The M1 Garand

base near the inside of the vertical face, rolling some flesh on the thumb between the long arm and the base. Press the long arm outward (toward your body) and slightly downward, and snap the clip ejector into place.

Hold the trigger housing at the rearmost portion with the left hand, vertical face to the front, open side to the right. Grasp the trigger guard at the latch end, and place the wings astride the base of the trigger housing at the same point from which the trigger guard was removed. Swing the trigger guard down and to the left, then slide it forward into position.

Replace the safety by inserting the finger piece through its slot in the base of the housing, and seat the safety stud in its hole in the side of the housing. In seating the safety, some downward pressure against the short arm of the clip ejector is necessary. Push the finger piece to its forward position. Swing the trigger guard to its open position and replace the hammer in a half-cocked position, making sure that the toe is in front of the hammer stop. Align the holes in the hammer, the housing, and the wings of the trigger guard and insert the hammer pin, oscillating the trigger guard and hammer, seating the pin fully. Do not force it.

Assemble the hammer spring housing, hammer spring, and hammer spring plunger into one unit. Place the trigger housing on the table, open side to your front, vertical face to left, hammer up. Place the nose of the plunger in its seat on the hammer, being sure that the cutaway portion of the hammer spring housing is toward the safety. With the palm of the left hand over the hammer hold the hammer spring housing, hammer spring, and hammer spring plunger in place with the fingers of the left hand.

Insert the finger piece of the trigger through the trigger slot, so that the notch is above the base of the housing. Allow the wings of the hammer spring housing to straddle the sear pin. When properly placed you can see the ends of the sear pin through the holes in the wings. Press back on the finger piece of the trigger with the right forefinger, and push on the sear with the right thumb. Steady the hammer spring housing with the left fingers. Press down quickly on the sear, align the holes for the trigger pin, and insert the trigger pin to its head only.

To seat the head of the trigger pin, turn your right hand palm up and grasp the trigger group so that the top of the hammer is toward the body and the open side is up, the right thumb in rear of the sear, the first and second fingers grasping the vertical face. Apply a sudden squeeze by strongly attempting to close the right hand and at the same time seat the trigger pin by applying pressure on its head with the left thumb.

DISASSEMBLY AND ASSEMBLY OF THE STOCK GROUP

To **disassemble the stock group**, remove the butt plate by taking out the top and bottom screws. Withdrawing the long lower butt plate screw will also free the rear swivel which can be pulled down and out of the stock.

Next remove the stock ferrule by driving out the stock ferrule pin from left to right, then carefully wriggling the ferrule off the lip of the stock.

227

The M1 Garand

Remove the stock swivel by unscrewing the stock ferrule screw, the end of which is peened over to prevent its coming loose. If this screw is removed, it will have to be replaced with a new one.

Reassembly is the reverse of the above procedures.

A WORD ABOUT MAINTENANCE

Do not overlubricate your M1 Garand. Too much oil attracts dust and grit which will form an abrasive paste and cause parts to wear excessively. A single drop of oil, blotted with a clean cloth, is sufficient for all friction points. A light coating of a good gun grease is sufficient for the bolt track. The most important lubrication points for your M1 Garand are: the inside of the bolt lug housing on the operating rod and the right bolt lug, the bottom of the barrel against which the operating rod rides and the upper rear of the receiver against which the bolt rides, to prevent excessive wear.

When cleaning your rifle's bore with steel cleaning rods, always use a muzzle or bore guide to prevent excessive wear at the muzzle. Better yet, use brass or nylon-coated cleaning rods.

If you are firing World War II surplus ammunition with corrosive primers, clean the rifle as soon after use as possible. **The corrosive primers used in M1 or M2 military ammunition made before 1954 can cause pitting and rust to develop in the bore and on the face of the bolt in a matter of days.** Either swab well with G.I. bore cleaner which was specially formulated to remove the corrosive residue, or use hot, soapy water in the following manner. Note that this is not a "G.I." procedure but will remove all elements of corrosive residue if performed thoroughly as soon after shooting as possible.

Dismount the rifle and remove the handguards, operating rod and assembly, bolt and gas cylinder. Insert a funnel into the breech end of the barrel and pour a quart of boiling soapy water through the bore. Scrub with clean patches until dry. Repeat, then rinse with clean, boiling water. Run several oily patches through the bore after it has cooled enough to be handled, blot all moisture away from the exterior and wipe down with an oily patch. Reassemble the rifle. Repeat this process for the gas cylinder and for the bolt after disassembly. Inspect the cleaned part two days later to make certain that all corrosive residue was removed. If you see signs of corrosion, repeat the entire procedure.

APPENDIX H
THE IMPORTANCE OF BARREL GAUGES

M1 Garand collectors are not only interested in original finish and correct configuration, but, also the rifle's bore. This concern with bore condition arises primarily because M1 Garand collectors often shoot their rifles whereas collectors of other types of firearms rarely do and so tend to disregard bore condition. M1 Garand collectors will check the muzzle, gauge the breech and check headspace for tolerances.

When serious M1 Garand collectors contemplate a purchase, they will have with four important items: 1) a throat erosion gauge, 2) a dummy .30-06 cartridge, 3) a set of headspace gauges and 4) this book, see Figure H-1. Military surplus and commercial erosion gauges are available, although hard to find.

Figure H-1.

GAUGE, BREECH, BORE

Commonly called a throat erosion gauge, it measures the wear at the breech end of the barrel at the lead where the rifling begins. This area is also known as the "throat." The diameter of the throat is important. When the propellant ignites and drives the bullet into the rifling, not only should the distance between the case mouth and the lead be short but the lead should be symmetrical so that the bullet is oriented as close to 90 degrees in relation to the bore axis as possible. Since the hot propellant gases also erode the bore in the throat, enlarging it, the path of the bullet into the lead will be deflected and accuracy will suffer.

The erosion gauge is tapered along its length and calibrated from "0" to "10." A "4-5" reading on the gauge would indicate that half the barrel life is gone and accuracy may suffer accordingly. U.S. Army specifications considered a "5" reading acceptable. A barrel that has been "shot out" will register as high as "9" or "10" (0.31 inch).

229

The M1 Garand

DUMMY CARTRIDGE

The dummy cartridge is used to check the condition of the muzzle. Worn rifling at the muzzle end, or dents or cuts will greatly affect accuracy. Insert the bullet end of the cartridge into the muzzle. The bullet should fit tightly and there should be a 1/8-inch gap between the case mouth and the barrel. A smaller gap between the barrel and case mouth of less than 1/8 inch indicates muzzle wear which will affect accuracy. If the case mouth touches the barrel, the bore is too worn to be used.

HEADSPACE GAUGES

Headspace in the M1 Garand is the distance between the bolt face when locked closed and the forward shoulder of the chamber. If too tight, a cartridge case will not have room to expand and excess pressure may back out primers or even blow them out, releasing hot propellant gases. If headspace is too loose, the fired cartridge case will expand back against the bolt face, stretching the neck, or if excessive, the case body. If the case neck stretches enough to split, hot propellant gas will be released but because the case body has expanded behind it to seal the chamber, it will be driven down the bore. If the case neck breaks, the part of the case may remain in the chamber after extraction and require the use of a headless shell extractor. If the headspace is enough to allow the case body to split, hot propellant gases will be released into the unsealed chamber and may injure the shooter, and will certainly injure the rifle. In the worst case, the cartridge may stretch enough to provide room for the propellant to actually detonate. This could fracture the receiver with fatal results to the shooter and bystanders.

To ensure that the rifle can be fired safely, headspace specifications have been established that must be adhered to within 0.006 inch. Official Department of Defense specifications for the M1 Garand chamber are not less than 1.940 inches and not greater than 1.950 inches long. Acceptance standards when new, were headspace not less than 1.942 inches and not more than 1.944 inches long.

Headspace in the M1 Garand is measured using three separate gauges. Headspace gauges used for the M1 Garand must have a 45-degree bevel on the edges of the head. If they do not, you must remove the ejector before checking headspace.

Place the headspace gauge on the face of the bolt and ease the operating rod forward. The best results can be obtained by disengaging the operating rod from the bolt and moving the bolt by hand. Use the gauges in the following order:

1) **No-Go Gauge (1.946 inches)**. The bolt should not close completely on the "No-Go Gauge" and the bolt lug should remain above the receiver. If the bolt lug does touch the receiver, then repeat the process using the "Field" gauge.

2) **Field Gauge (1.9502 inches)**. The bolt should not close on the "Field Gauge." If it does, headspace is excessive and the M1 Garand should not be fired.

3) **Go Gauge (1.9401 inches)**. After determining that the M1 Garand's headspace is not excessive, use the "Go" gauge to make sure that the chamber is not too tight. The bolt should close completely.

See "Aids for Collectors" following the Appendices about acquiring these gauges.

NOTE: Anyone shooting a high-power rifle must examine the rifle and the fired cases periodically for signs of excess headspace or other damage. The first step is the examination of the primer of a newly fired cartridge case. The primer is set slightly below the rim of the unfired case by the manufacturer. After firing, rub your thumbnail over the end of the case. If the primer can be felt it is because excess pressure has begun to push it from its seat. Examine the case for other signs of excess pressure such as bulges near the neck or shoulder or just forward of the head. If you note a protruding primer or other signs of increased pressure, do not fire the rifle again until it has been checked thoroughly by a competent gunsmith.

And, of course, no responsible, thinking person will ever shoot any firearm without wearing effective eye and ear protection.

APPENDIX I
ATTACHING THE MODEL 1907 LEATHER SLING

MODEL 1907 LEATHER SLING

Following are simplified instructions for mounting the M1907 sling on your M1 Garand.

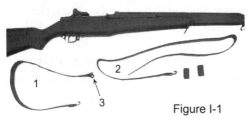

Lay the rifle sights down and muzzle pointing to the right.

Lay out the two pieces of the sling, short piece on the left (1), long piece on the right (2), both with the

Figure I-1

smooth side pointing to the bottom of the rifle, Figure I-1.

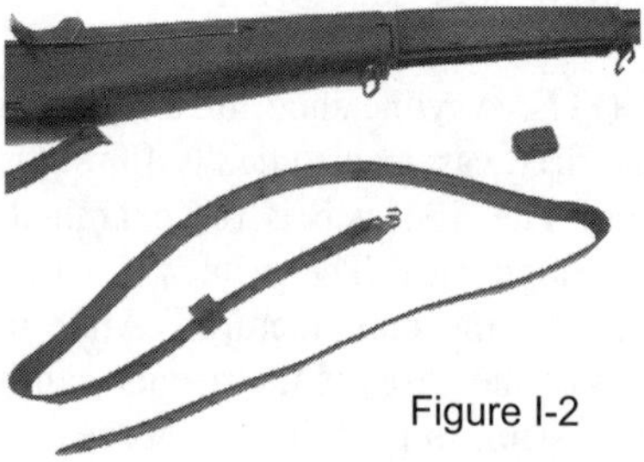

Pick up one keeper and slide it over the free end of the long piece to about five inches from the hook, see Figure I-2.

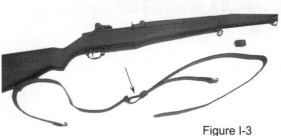

Figure I-2

Slide the D-ring (3) on the short piece over the free end of the long piece. Take the free end of the long piece and feed it back through the keeper so that it forms a loop with the D-ring in its bight (arrow). Figure I-3.

Slide the second keeper over the free end (called the feed end), then slide the free end through the forward sling swivel, then back through the

second keeper so that it forms a second loop with the sling swivel at its bight, see Figure I-4.

Hook the clawed end of the long piece into the

Figure I-3

232

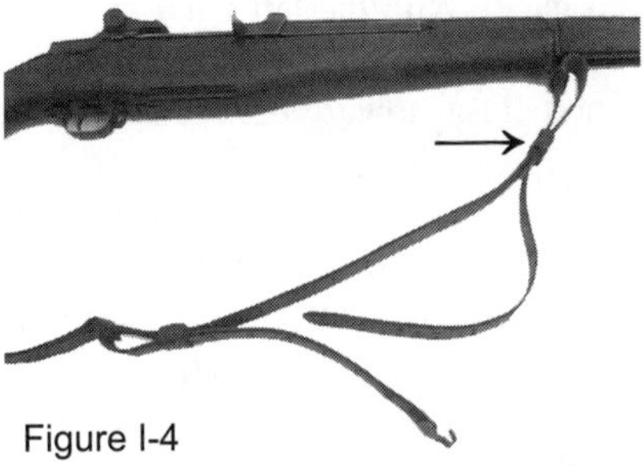

The M1 Garand

Figure I-4

ninth set of holes on the feed end.

Slide the hooks on the short end through the rear sling swivel and pull it tight and hook it into the feed end as close to the long end's claw as needed, see Figure I-5, arrow.

To use the sling as a shooting support, unhook the short end claw and let it dangle loose. Slide your hand between the inside strap and the feed end, then twist your wrist over the top of the inside strap

Figure I-5

and to the left so that the sling lies against the back of your hand. If the sling is adjusted properly—ninth feed hole—the buttstock should wedge tightly against your shoulder. If your arms are longer or shorter than average, adjust the claw in the feed end up or down until you achieve a tight "wedge" fit.

MODEL 1923 WEB SLING

The Model 1923 web sling, see Figure I-6, is seldom encountered but the following instructions will assist in the installation for those lucky enough to find one.

1. Lay the rifle on a flat surface, sights down and muzzle pointing left.

2. Hold the long strap with the buckle end in the right hand with the sewn fold upright. Insert the loose or "feed" end through the rear sling swivel and pull the feed end toward the butt of the rifle.

Figure I-6

3. Pick up the short strap and holding the D-ring in the left hand with the sewed fold down, hold the feed end in the right hand above the trigger housing and insert it through the rear swivel.

233

The M1 Garand

4. Pick up the keeper with the right hand. With the left hand take the feed end of the long strap and insert it through the keeper so that the thumb piece of the keeper faces up and closes toward the muzzle.

5. With the left hand pick up the small buckle, holding it so that the crossbars are up and the thumb piece is toward the butt. Hold feed end of the short strap in right hand and insert the end up through the small buckle at the slot nearest the thumb piece, then back down through the slot farthest from the thumb piece, allowing about 8 inches to come through the buckle.

6. Take the feed end of the long strap again in the left hand and bring it up through the D-ring on the short strap. Fold the long strap back over the top of the D-ring and insert the end through the keeper.

7. Still holding the feed end of the long strap, bring it up through the slot of the large buckle nearest the sewed fold of the long strap and continue it back down through the second slot from the sewed fold, allowing 3 or 4 inches of the strap to come through.

8. Again pick up the feed end of the short strap and bring it up through the large buckle at the slot nearest the thumb piece and back down through the one remaining open slot. Continue the end of the strap back to the small buckle and insert it up through the slot farthest from the thumb piece and down through the middle slot of the small buckle.

9. To tighten the sling, grasp the inside strap with the right hand and force it firmly toward the butt of the rifle, at the same time with the left hand forcing the outside strap toward the muzzle. Close the keeper to hold the sling in its taut position.

10. When the sling is properly adjusted and tightened, the large buckle will be located just below the stock ferrule swivel and just above the small buckle. The keeper will be well down toward the D-ring on the short strap. This leaves the sling free of obstruction above and below the trigger guard. The small buckle should be in a position above the balance of the rifle to prevent interference with the left hand while performing the manual of arms.

The M1 Garand

M1 Sling, Improved

Figure I-7

1. Place the rifle on a flat surface, sights down, and muzzle pointing to the left.

2. Snap the hook into the butt swivel with the hook opening out.

3. Pick up the strap, holding the buckle end in the left hand with the sewn fold down. With the right hand insert the feed end of the strap down through the D-ring on the hook and pull the feed end toward the muzzle, Figure I-7.

4. Holding the buckle in the left hand, insert the feed end of the sling through the buckle slot nearest the sewed fold. Work the buckle toward the butt of the rifle until it is six or seven inches from the butt swivel as shown in Figure I-7. Insert the feed end of the sling through the remaining slot of the buckle, which faces outward from the sewed fold.

Figure I-8

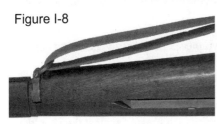

5. With the left hand pick up the keeper. With the right hand take the feed end of the sling through the keeper so that the thumb piece of the keeper is uppermost and closes toward the butt of the rifle, Figure I-8.

6. Insert the feed end of the sling through the front swivel and pull it taut.

Figure I-9

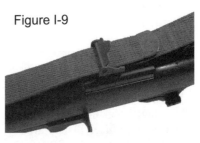

7. Take the feed end of the sling in the left hand, fold it toward the butt and insert it through the keeper. Work the keeper and feed end of the sling in the direction of the butt and as close to the buckle as possible. Tighten the sling by pulling the feed end taut. Close the keeper, Figure I-9.

APPENDIX J
GLOSSARY

Aperture. The opening or peep for the eye in the rear sight.

Black Oxide. A chemical process that provides a black coating of oxide to steel to prevent glare and rust.

Bluing. A chemical or heat process by which the top layers of steel or iron are oxidized to a blue-black color. The objective is to darken the metal to prevent glare, rather than to prevent rusting.

BMB, BMP, BMR. Inspection stamps used by the Italian firearms-manufacturing firm, Breda.

Bore. The interior of a firearm barrel. Rifled barrels have tracks, called lands and grooves, that spiral from the breech to muzzle to impart spin to a bullet to stabilize it in flight.

Braze. The process of joining two pieces of metal by soldering, usually with brass as the joining metal.

Breech. The chamber end of the barrel or barrel insert.

Butt. Refers to the end of the stock which presses against the shoulder.

Butt Plate. Metal plate or cap made to fit the end of the buttstock to prevent splintering.

Carburize. A process whereby heat drives carbon into steel in order to harden the alloy.

Cartouche. A stamp impressed into wood or metal. Cartouches applied to firearms usually denote quality control acceptance or are used to identify a maker. In the case of the M1 Garand, the cartouche usually refers to the Ordnance Department's final stamp of acceptance. This consisted of the initials of the armory over those of an authorized officer or the commanding officer of that armory, enclosed within a box that varied roughly between 0.75 and 1.0 inch.

Casting. The process of pouring molten metal into a mold.

The M1 Garand

Clean and Repair Program. A procedure instituted at Springfield Armory after World War II to rebuilt M1 Garands used during the war.

Crossed Cannon Cartouche. Quality-control-check mark applied by U.S. Army Ordnance Department Inspectors. It consists of two crossed cannons behind a belt. It is sometimes referred to as the "Ordnance Wheel" by collectors.

Crown. To machine the muzzle of a barrel to produce a rounded or rebated end to protect the ends of the rifling.

Crown/BNP. British Nitro Proof. Stamped on firearms manufactured in or sold through United Kingdom in 1955 and after.

Defense Acceptance Stamp. The Ordnance Department cartouche used after September-October 1953 to denote final acceptance. It replaced the standard cartouche box containing the initials of the Armory over the authorized or commanding officer. The new cartouche consisted of the national eagle symbol under three stars enclosed within a 0.50- or 0.375-inch box.

De-mill. De-militarize: to destroy a firearm by cutting or crushing the receiver.

En-Bloc Clip. A metal container made of spring steel which held eight cartridges for the M1 Garand.

Federal Stock Number. Eleven-digit identifying code applied to all items in the Department of Defense supply system between 1948 and 1974 until the system was replaced by the fourteen-digit National Stock Number system.

FKF. Danish initials for the Forsvarets Krigsmaterial Forvaltning (Defense War Material Administration).

Forge. The process by which metal is formed to shape by repeated heating and hammering.

HMAK. Danish initials for the Haerens Material Kommando (Army Material Command).

The M1 Garand

HTK. Danish initials for the Haerens Tekniske Korps (Army Technical Corps).

In the white. A steel or other metal part left in its natural "white" color without the application of any finish.

Left Side. When held in the firing position, that side of the firearm on your left.

Milled. To shape or dress metal using a rotary cutter.

Muzzle. Forward end of the barrel.

National Stock Number. Fourteen-digit code applied to all equipment and their parts in federal inventory. The NSN replaced the earlier federal stock number which in turn replaced the even-earlier drawing number.

Parkerize. A chemical process by which dilute phosphoric acid is applied to steel to confer a high degree of rustproofing and to eliminate glare and reflections. Many parts of the M1 Garand were Parkerized after being lightly sandblasted to produce better adhesion.

PB. Inspection stamp used by the Italian firearms-manufacturing firm, Beretta.

Proof. A quality-control inspection and testing of a part. When applied to firearms, it usually involves firing an oversized charge to test the integrity of the barrel. Also refers to the process of marking the firearm and/or part to show that it has been proof-tested.

Receiver. That part of the firearm to which are attached the barrel, trigger assembly, bolt assembly and stock.

Refurbish. To rebuild and otherwise restore to full operational condition an M1 Garand or other military firearm. Refurbishments done for the U.S. military are governed by specific procedures.

Right Side. When held in the firing position, that side of the firearm on your right.

The M1 Garand

Sans Serif. A serif is a short line or stroke projecting, usually at an angle, from a number or letter. This text is an example of a type face with serifs. This sentence is an example of a sans serif type face.

Stake. To upset the metal of one part into or against another to hold both in place. Usually done with a hammer and punch.

Stamp. The process of forming metal blanks into parts by use of a hammer and die.

Spline. The raised ridge inside the gas cylinder forward band which fits into matching grooves in the forward part of the barrel.

Springfield Armory. The national armory and manufacturer of U.S. military firearms established by the federal government in 1794 at Springfield, Massachusetts. Not to be confused with the private, commercial company at Geneseo, Illinois.

Weld. To join to metals by melting the edges or surfaces together with high heat.

APPENDIX K
BIBLIOGRAPHY

Barnes, Frank, *Cartridges of the World*, DBI Books Inc., 4092 Commercial Ave., Northbrook, IL 60062, 5th Edition, 1985.

Beach, 1st Lieutenant S.H., *History of Small Arms Procurement, 1939-1945, Ordnance Department, U.S. Army*, reprinted by Springfield Research Service, PO Box 4181, Silver Spring, MD 20914.

Brophy, Lieutenant Colonel William S., *The Springfield Armory 1890-1948*, Andrew Mowbray Publishers, PO Box 460, Lincoln, RI 02865, 1991.

Canfield, Bruce N., *A Collector's Guide to the M1 Garand and M1 Carbine*, Andrew Mowbray Publishers, Lincoln, RI, 1988.

Cole, M.H., *U.S. Military Knives, Bayonets and Machetes: Book III*, M.H. Cole, 501 Ridge Road, Birmingham, AL 35206, 1979.

Duff, Scott A., *The M1 Garand: Owner's Guide*, Scott Duff, PO Box 414, Export, PA 15632, 1995.

Duff, Scott A., *The M1 Garand: Post World War II*, Scott Duff, PO Box 414, Export, PA 15632, 1989.

Duff, Scott A., *The M1 Garand: Serial Numbers and Data Sheets*, Scott Duff, PO Box 414, Export, PA 15632, 1995.

Duff, Scott A., *The M1 Garand: World War II*, Scott Duff, PO Box 414, Export, PA 15632, 1993.

Ezell, Edward C., *Small Arms of the World*, Stackpole Books, Harrisburg, PA 17105, 12th Edition, 1983.

Green, Constance McLaughlin, Harry C. Thomson, and Peter C. Roots, *The United States Army in World War II; Technical Services–Ordnance Department: Planning Munitions for War*. Washington, DC, 1955.

The M1 Garand

Hatcher, Major General Julian S., *Book of the Garand*, The Gun Room Press, Highland Park, NJ, 1983.

Hoffschmidt, E.J., *Know Your M1 Garand*, Blacksmith Corporation, Stamford, CT, 1975.

Hogg, Ian V. and John Weeks, *Military Small Arms of the 20th Century*, DBI Books, Northfield, IL 60093, 7th Edition, 2000.

Janzen, Jerry L., *Bayonets from Janzen's Notebook*, PO Box 2863, Tulsa, OK 74107, 1984.

Karwan, Charles W., "The CMP: Past, Present and Future," *American Rifleman*, November 2004.

Marshall, S.L.A., *Battlefield Analysis of Infantry Weapons*, reprinted by Desert Publications, Cornville, AZ, 1984.

McLean, Donald B., *The M1 Garand Rifles: M1, M1C and M1D*, Desert Publications, Cornville, AZ, 1966.

Phillips, William G., "Evolution of the Pocket-Type Rifle Belt in the United States Service," *Journal of the Company of Military Historians*, Vol. 22, Spring, 1970.

Pyle, Billy, *Ordnance Tools, Accessories & Appendages of the M1 Rifle*, G.S. Publications, Houston, TX, 1988.

Rila, Carter, "The Development of U.S. Army Infantry Equipments, 1903-1956," *Journal of the Company of Military Historians*, Vol. 21, No. 2., Summer, 1969.

Senich, Peter S., *The Complete Book of U.S. Sniping*, Paladin Press, Boulder, CO, 1988.

Senich, Peter S., *The Long Range War: Sniping in Vietnam*, Paladin Press, Boulder, CO, 1994.

The M1 Garand

Shaffer, James B., Lee A. Rutledge and R. Stephen Dorsey, *Gun Tools: Their History and Identification*, Collectors' Library, PO Box 263, Eugene, OR 97440, 1992.

Stevens, R. Blake, *U.S. Rifle M14 from John Garand to the M21*, Collector Grade Publications, PO Box 1046, Cobourg, Ontario, Canada K9A 4W5. (http://www.collectorgrade.com)

Stoddard, Simeon, *Finding Guide (To Winchester M1 Garand Drawings)*: *MS 63*, Armax, Volume 5, 1995, Buffalo Bill Historical Center, Cody, WY 82414.

Stoddard, Simeon, *Finding Guide (To Winchester M1 Garand Drawings)*: *MS 63*, Armax, Volume 6, 1996, Buffalo Bill Historical Center, Cody, WY 82414.

Tantum, William H., IV, *Sniper Rifles of Two World Wars*, Museum Restoration Service, Bloomfield, Ontario, 1967.

Wallack, L.R., *American Rifle Design and Performance*, Winchester Press, New York, NY 10017, 1977.

Field and Technical Manuals

Hand & Rifle Grenades, Field Manual 23-30, April 14, 1949, Department of the Army, Government Printing Office, Washington, DC, 1949.

Ordnance Maintenance, U.S. Rifles, Cal. .30 M1, Technical Manual TM 9-1275, November 6, 1942, War Department, Ordnance Office, Government Printing Office, Washington, DC, 1942.

Ordnance Maintenance, U.S. Rifles, Cal. .30 M1, M1C (Sniper's) and M1D (Sniper's), Technical Manual TM 9-1275, June 17, 1947, War Department, Ordnance Office, Government Printing Office, Washington, DC, 1947.

Technical Manual, TM 9-1904, *Ammunition Inspection Guide*, War Department, Washington, DC, 1944.

Technical Manual 9-1005-222-12, *Operator and Organizational Maintenance Manual Including Repair Parts and Special Tool List for*

The M1 Garand

Rifle, Caliber .30 M1; Rifle, Caliber .30 M1C and Rifle, Caliber .30 M1D, War Department, Government Printing Office, Washington, DC, June 1947.

Technical Manual 9-1005-222-12P/1, *Operator and Organizational Maintenance Manual Including Repair Parts and Special Tool List for Caliber .30 U.S. Rifle M1 (National Match)*, Headquarters, Department of the Army, Government Printing Office, Washington, DC, July 1961.

Technical Manual 9-1005-222-12, *Rifle, Caliber .30, M1, Rifle, Caliber .30, M1C (Sniper's), Rifle, Caliber .30, M1D (Sniper's)*, March 17, 1969, Headquarters, Department of the Army, Government Printing Office, Washington, DC, 1969.

Technical Manual 9-6131, *Ordnance Maintenance, Telescope, M84*, June 1954, Department of the Army, Washington, D.C. 1981.

Technical Bulletin PMG-4, Department of the Army, U.S. Army, 13 December 1951.

Technical Manual 9-2205, Department of the Army, U.S. Army, May 1952.

Technical Manual 9-2210 (TO39A-5A-6), Departments of the Army and Air Force, Department of Defense, Washington, DC, June 1953.

Technical Manual 9-1900 (TO IIA-I-20), Departments of the Army and Air Force, Department of Defense, Washington, DC, June 1956.

Technical Manual 9-2200 (TO IIW3-I-5), Departments of the Army and Air Force, Department of Defense, Washington, DC, October 1956.

U.S. Rifle, Caliber .30, M1, Basic Field Manual 23-5, July 20, 1940, War Department, Ordnance Office, Government Printing Office, Washington, DC, 1940.

U.S. Rifle, Caliber .30, M1, Basic Field Manual 23-5, July 30, 1943, War Department, Ordnance Office, Government Printing Office, Washington, DC, 1943.

The M1 Garand

U.S. Rifle, Caliber .30, M1, Field Manual 23-5 (TO 39A-5AC-II), Departments of the Army and Air Force, Department of Defense, Washington, DC, October 1953.

U.S. Rifle, Caliber .30, M1, Field Manual 23-5, September 26, 1958, Headquarters, Department of the Army, Government Printing Office, Washington, DC, 1958.

U.S. Rifle, Caliber .30, M1, Field Manual 23-5, May 17, 1965, Headquarters, Department of the Army, Government Printing Office, Washington, DC, 1965.

AIDS FOR COLLECTORS

The experienced M1 Garand collector not only searches for those rifles that are as original as possible, but also those with an excellent bore and in fine operating condition. The M1 Garand collector is somewhat unique among firearms collectors in that he or she is as concerned with shooting condition as with finish and originality.

Serious M1 Garand collectors will acquire and use a set of headspace gauges, a throat erosion gauge, and a dummy bullet to check the rifle's headspace and the condition of the throat and muzzle. These gauges have become difficult to find in recent years. North Cape Publications recommends that the serious collector desiring a set of these gauges acquire them from Brownells, 200 South Front Street, Montezuma, IA 50171 (800 741-0015). They offer sets and individual gauges for either the .30-06 or the 7.62 mm NATO (.308) M1 Garand.

The authors recommend the Garand Collectors Association to those interested in the M1 Garand and its accessories. This unique organization established in 1968 publishes a 24-page newsletter quarterly on the M1 Garand, its history, development and accessories. Contact the GCA at P.O. Box 181, Richmond, KY 40475.

The *Garand Stand Report* is an excellent quarterly publication dedicated to understanding the M1 Garand. Again, the authors recommend it to the interested M1 collector. For further information, write to, Billy Pyle, Editor, G.S. Publications, PO Box 34005, Houston, TX 77234-4005.

ABOUT THE AUTHORS AND EDITOR

Joe Poyer is the author of more than 400 magazine articles on firearms, the modern military, military history and personal security. He has written and published twelve novels with worldwide sales exceeding five million copies and authored or coauthored nine nonfiction books on the modern military from other publishers.

He is the editorial director and publisher of North Cape Publications®, Inc., which publishes the "For Collectors Only®" and "A Shooter's and Collector's Guide" series of books for firearms collectors and shooters. In these series, he has written or coauthored: *The .45-70 Springfield*; *U.S. Winchester Trench and Riot Guns, and Other U.S. Combat Shotguns*; *The M1 Garand, 1936 to 1957*; *The SKS Carbine*; *The M14-Type Rifle*; *The SAFN-49 Battle Rifle*; *The Swedish Mauser Rifles*; *The M16/AR15 Rifle*; *The Model 1903 Springfield Rifle and Its Variations*; *The American Krag Rifle and Carbine*; *Swiss Magazine Loading Rifles, 1869 to 1958;* and *The AK-47 and AK-74 Kalashnikov Rifles and Their Variations*.

Mr. Poyer has served as editor of the following magazines: *Safe & Secure Living*; *International Military Review*; *International Naval Review* and as field editor for *International Combat Arms*. He is currently at work on a new book in the "For Collectors Only" series, *The U.S. Government .45 ACP Pistol*.

Mr. Poyer was the on-camera Military Affairs Analyst and Reporter for a major television station in Los Angeles, California. He also imported the very fine L1A1A inch pattern FAL rifles from Australia in the late 1980s.

Craig Riesch is a well-known collector and scholar of U.S. military small arms. He is the author of *The U.S. M1 Carbine: Wartime Production* and was the coauthor of *The .45-70 Springfield* and *The M1 Garand, 1936 to 1957*. He also edited *The American Krag Rifle and Carbine* and *The Swiss Magazine Loading Rifles, 1869-1958*, all in the "For Collectors Only"series plus *The AK-47 and AK-74 Kalashnikov Rifles* in the "Shooter's and Collector's" series. Both series are guides to antique and collectible modern firearms identification and verification.

Mr. Riesch has spent a great deal of time studying U.S. military firearms and is consulted by many collectors for authentication of military and civilian arms. He has been a collector himself for over forty years. Mr. Riesch is a U.S. Army combat veteran and served in Vietnam during the period of the Tet Offensive. He worked for 33 years as a product operations manager for a major defense company.

Simeon Stoddard served as Curator and Assistant Curator of the Cody Firearms Museum and the Archival Assistant for the McCracken Research Library at the Buffalo Bill Historical Center, Cody, Wyoming. A graduate of Brigham Young University in History, Mr. Stoddard has a long-time fascination with firearms and their development. He started competitive shooting at the age of six, and has been an active collector of military firearms since the age of fourteen. He is a student of the M1 Garand, particularly those of Winchester production. While at the Cody Firearms Museum, Mr. Stoddard was engaged in a massive program to catalog and review a complete set of original M1 design and fixture drawings donated to the Cody Firearms Museum by Mr. Peter Alcock and the U.S. Repeating Arms Company.

BOOKS FROM
NORTH CAPE PUBLICATIONS®, INC.

The books in the "For Collectors Only®" and "A Shooter's and Collector's Guide" series are designed to provide the firearms collector with an accurate record of the markings, dimensions and finish found on an original firearm as it was shipped from the factory. As changes to any and all parts are listed by serial number range, the collector can quickly assess not only whether or not the overall firearm is correct as issued, but whether or not each and every part is original for the period of the particular firearm's production. "For Collectors Only" and "A Shooter's and Collector's Guide" books make each collector and shooter an "expert."

FOR COLLECTORS ONLY® SERIES

Swiss Magazine Loading Rifles, 1869 to 1958, by Joe Poyer ($19.95). The Swiss were the first to adopt a repeating rifle as general issue to all troops in 1869. The rifle was the Vetterli, a clever blend of Swiss and American engineering. In 1889, the Swiss adopted a small-bore rifle with a straight pull bolt and a box magazine, the Schmidt-Rubin, that somewhat resembled that developed around the same time for the British Lee-Enfield rifles. The design was so successful, that with relatively minor changes and upgrades, it remained in service until 1958 when it was replaced by a semiautomatic rifle. As with all the books in the "For Collectors Only" series, there is a complete part-by-part description for both the Vetterli and Schmidt-Rubin rifles in all their variations by serial number range, plus a history of their development and use, their cleaning, maintenance and how to shoot them safely and accurately.

The American Krag Rifle and Carbine, by Joe Poyer, edited by Craig Riesch ($19.95). A new look on a part-by-part basis at the first magazine repeating service arm adopted for general service in American military history. It was the arm first adopted for smokeless powder and it required new manufacturing techniques and processes to be developed for its production at Springfield Armory. The Krag was an outstanding weapon that helped define the course of American arms development over the next fifty years. In this new text, the Krag is redefined in terms of its development. Old shibboleths, mischaracterizations and misinterpretations are laid to rest and a true picture of this amazingly collectible rifle and carbine emerges. The author has also devised a monthly serial number chart

248

from production, quarterly and annual reports from Springfield Armory and the Chief of Ordnance to the Secretary of War.

The Model 1903 Springfield Rifle and Its Variations (2nd edition, revised and expanded), by Joe Poyer ($22.95). Includes every model of the Model 1903 from the ramrod bayonet to the Model 1903A4 Sniper rifle. Every part description includes changes by serial number range, markings and finish. Every model is described and identified. Abundant color and black-and-white photos and line drawings of parts to show details precisely. 480 pages.

The .45-70 Springfield, by Joe Poyer and Craig Riesch ($16.95), covers the entire range of .45-caliber "trapdoor" Springfield arms, the gun that really won the West. "Virtually a mini-encyclopedia . . . this reference piece is a must," Phil Spangenberger, *Guns & Ammo*.

U.S. Winchester Trench and Riot Guns and Other U.S. Combat Shotguns (2nd edition, revised), by Joe Poyer ($16.95). Describes the elusive and little-known "Trench Shotgun" and all other combat shotguns used by U.S. military forces. "U.S. military Models 97 and 12 Trench and Riot Guns, their parts, markings [and] dimensions [are examined] in great detail . . . a basic source of information for collectors," C.R. Suydam, *Gun Report*.

The U.S. M1 Carbine: Wartime Production (4th edition revised), by Craig Riesch ($16.95), describes the four models of M1 Carbines from all ten manufacturers. Complete with codes for every part by serial number range. "The format makes it extremely easy to use. The book is a handy reference for beginning or experienced collectors," Bruce Canfield, Author of *M1 Garand and M1 Carbine*.

The M1 Garand, 1936 to 1957 (4th edition, revised and expanded), by Joe Poyer and Craig Riesch ($19.95). "The book covers such important identification factors as manufacturer's markings, proof marks, final acceptance cartouches stampings, heat treatment lot numbers . . . there are detailed breakdowns of . . . every part . . . in minute detail. This 216 page . . . volume is easy to read and full of identification tables, parts diagrams and other crucial graphics that aid in determining the originality of your M1 and/or its component parts," Phil Spangenberger, *Guns & Ammo*.

249

Winchester Lever Action Repeating Firearms, by Arthur Pirkle
    Volume 1, The Models of 1866, 1873 & 1876 ($19.95)
    Volume 2, The Models of 1886 and 1892 ($19.95)
    Volume 3, The Models of 1894 and 1895 ($19.95)
These famous lever action repeaters are completely analyzed part-by-part by serial number range in this first new book on these fine weapons in twenty years. ". . . book is truly for the serious collector . . . Mr. Pirkle's scholarship is excellent and his presentation of the information . . . is to be commended," H.G.H., *Man at Arms*.

The SKS Carbine (3rd revised and expanded edition), by Steve Kehaya and Joe Poyer ($16.95). The SKS Carbine "is profusely illustrated, articulately researched and covers all aspects of its development as well as . . . other combat guns used by the USSR and other Communist bloc nations. Each component . . . from stock to bayonet lug, or lack thereof, is covered along with maintenance procedures . . . because of Kehaya's and Poyer's book, I have become the leading expert in West Texas on [the SKS]," Glen Voorhees, Jr., *Gun Week*.

British Enfield Rifles, by Charles R. Stratton
    Volume 1, SMLE (No. 1) Mk I and Mk III ($16.95)
"Stratton . . . does an admirable job of . . . making sense of . . . a seemingly hopeless array of marks and models and markings and apparently endless varieties of configurations and conversions . . . this is a book that any collector of SMLE rifles will want," Alan Petrillo, *The Enfield Collector's Digest*.

    Volume 2, The Lee-Enfield No. 4 and No. 5 Rifles ($16.95)
In Volume 2, "Skip" Stratton provides a concise but extremely thorough analysis of the famed British World War II rifle, the No. 4 Enfield, and the No. 5 Rifle, better known as the "Jungle Carbine." It's all here, markings, codes, parts, manufacturers and history of development and use.

    Volume 4, The Pattern 1914 and U.S. Model 1917 Rifles
    ($16.95)
In Volume 4, the author describes the events that led to the development of the British Pattern 1914 Enfield and its twin, the U.S Model 1917 Enfield rifle. The M1917 was produced in and used on the Western front in far greater numbers than was the M1903 Springfield. Skip Stratton

provides not only the usual part-by-part analysis of both rifles to show how the M1917 evolved from the Pattern 1914, but provides a cross-check of which parts are interchangeable. Included are the sniper and Pedersen Device variants.

The Mosin-Nagant Rifle (3rd revised and expanded edition), by Terence W. Lapin ($19.95). For some reason, in the more than 100 years that the Mosin-Nagant rifle has been in service around the world, not a single book has been written in English about this fine rifle. Now, just as interest in the Mosin-Nagant is exploding, Terence W. Lapin has written a comprehensive volume that covers all aspects and models from the Imperial Russian rifles to the Finnish, American, Polish, Chinese, Romanian and North Korean variations. His book has set a standard that future authors will find very difficult to best. Included are part-by-part descriptions of all makers, Russian, Chinese, American, Polish, Romanian, etc. Also includes all variants such as carbines and sniper rifles from all countries.

The Swedish Mauser Rifles, by Steve Kehaya and Joe Poyer ($19.95). The Swedish Mauser rifle is perhaps the finest of all military rifles manufactured in the late 19th and early 20th centuries. A complete history of the development and use of the Swedish Mauser rifles is provided as well as a part-by-part description of each component. All 24 models are described and a complete description of the sniper rifles and their telescopic sights is included. All markings, codes, regimental and other military markings are charted and explained. A thorough and concise explanation of the Swedish Mauser rifle, both civilian and military.

A SHOOTER'S AND COLLECTOR'S GUIDE SERIES
The AK-47 and AK-74 Kalashnikov Rifles and Their Variations, by Joe Poyer ($22.95). The AK-47 and its small-caliber replacement, the AK-74, symbolize for Americans the now-defunct Soviet empire and its support for wars of "national liberation." Author Joe Poyer has examined and described the Kalashnikov rifle on a part-by-part basis, pointing out the differences between the various types of receivers and other parts, as well as the differences between the AK and AKM models. A detailed survey of all models of the Kalashnikov rifle from the AK-47 to the AK-108 is included as are descriptions of those Kalashnikov rifles manufactured by various countries from China to Switzerland. Accessories issued to the soldier from bayonets to web gear are included. Instructions on shooting, selecting telescopic sights, ammunition and troubleshooting round out the book.

251

The M16/AR15 Rifle (2nd edition, revised and expanded), by Joe Poyer ($19.95). The M16 has been in service longer than any other rifle in the history of the United States military. Its civilian counterpart, the AR15, has recently replaced the M14 as the national match service rifle. This 140-page, profusely illustrated, large-format book examines the development, history and current and future use of the M16/AR15. It describes in detail all civilian AR15 rifles from more than a dozen different manufacturers and takes the reader step-by-step through the process of accurizing the AR15 into an extremely accurate target rifle. Ammunition, both military and civilian, is discussed and detailed assembly/disassembly and troubleshooting instructions are included.

The M14-Type Rifle (2nd edition), by Joe Poyer ($14.95). A study of the U.S. Army's last and short-lived .30-caliber battle rifle which became a popular military sniper and civilian high-power match rifle. A detailed look at the National Match M14 rifle, the M21 sniper rifle and the currently available civilian semiautomatic match rifles, receivers, parts and accessories, including the Chinese M14s. A guide to custom-building a service-type rifle or a match-grade, precision rifle. Includes a list of manufacturers and parts suppliers, plus the BATFE regulations that allow a shooter to build a legal look-alike M14-type rifle.

The SAFN-49 Battle Rifle, by Joe Poyer ($14.95). The SAFN-49, the predecessor of the Free World's battle rifle, the FAL, has long been neglected by arms historians and writers, but not by collectors. Developed in the 1930s at the same time as the M1 Garand and the SVT38/40, the SAFN-49 did not reach production, because of the Nazi invasion of Belgium, until after World War II. This study of the SAFN-49 provides a part-by-part examination of the four calibers in which the rifle was made. Also, contains a thorough discussion of the SAFN-49 Sniper Rifle and its telescopic sights, plus maintenance, assembly/disassembly, accurizing, restoration and shooting. A new exploded view and section view are included. The rifle's development and military use are also explained in detail.

COLLECTOR'S GUIDE TO MILITARY UNIFORMS

The "Collector's Guide to Military Uniforms" endeavors to do for the military uniform collector what the "For Collectors Only®" series does for the firearms collector. Books in this series are carefully researched using original sources; they are heavily illustrated with line drawings and

252

photographs, both period and contemporary, to provide a clear picture of development and use. Where uniforms and accouterments have been reproduced, comparisons between original and reproduction pieces are included so that the collector and historian can differentiate the two.

Campaign Clothing: Field Uniforms of the Indian War Army
    Volume 1, 1866–1871 ($12.95)
    Volume 2, 1872–1886 ($14.95)
Lee A. Rutledge has produced a unique perspective on the uniforms of the Army of the United States during the late Indian War period following the Civil War. He discusses what the soldier really wore when on campaign. No white hats and yellow bandanas here.

A Guide Book to U.S. Army Dress Helmets, 1872–1904, by Mark Kasal and Don Moore ($16.95).
From 1872 to 1904, the men and officers of the U.S. Army wore a fancy, plumed or spiked helmet on all dress occasions. As ubiquitous as they were in the late 19th century, they are extremely scarce today. Kasal and Moore have written a step-by-step, part-by-part analysis of both the Models 1872 and 1881 dress helmets and their history and use. Profusely illustrated with black-and-white and color photographs of actual helmets.

All of the above books can be obtained directly from **North Cape Publications®, Inc., P.O. Box 1027, Tustin, CA 92781** or by calling Toll Free 1-800 745-9714. Orders only to the toll-free number, please. For information, call 714 832-3621. Orders may also be placed by Fax (714 832-5302) or via e-mail to ncape@ix.netcom.com. CA residents add 7.75% sales tax. Postage is currently $3.95 for 1-2 books, $5.50 for 3-4 books, $7.95 for 5-8 books. Call, fax or e-mail for UPS and Federal Express rates, for postage on quantities of 9 or more books, and for foreign postage rates.

Also, visit our Internet Website at http://www.northcapepubs.com. Our complete, up-to-date book list can always be found there. Also check out our linked Online Magazine for the latest in firearms-related, magazine-quality articles and excerpts from our books.

M1 Garand Evaluation Sheet			
Receiver			
Serial number			
Markings, rear			
Drawing number			
Markings, other & location			
Finish–original?			
Clip Guide Ribs–high or low			
Clip Latch			
	Type	**Mfg'r**	**Replace With**
Manufacturer			
Markings			
Rear Sight Assembly			
Rear sight elevation pinion			
Windage knob			
Lock nut			
Rear sight base			
Aperture			
Rear sight cover			
Bolt			
Bolt body			
Extractor, blued or Parkerized			
Ejector/Spring			
Firing pin			
Barrel			
Original or refinished			
Dimensions: Length _____ @ Gas port _____ @ 3rd Step _____ Top _____ Bottom _____			
Crown, original or recut			
Markings: Ordnance stamp & location: Drawing # Other:			

M1 Garand Evaluation Sheet, cont.

Operating Rod Assembly

	Type	Mfg'r	Replace With
Operating rod			
Drawing #			
Operating rod spring, no. of coils			
Compensating spring, no. of coils			
Follower rod			
Operating rod catch			
Follower arm			
Follower arm pin			
Follower			
Bullet guide			

Trigger Assembly

Trigger housing			
Trigger guard			
Trigger/Sear			
Hammer			
Hammer spring plunger			
Hammer spring, no. of coils			
Safety			

Gas Cylinder Assembly

Gas cylinder			
Front sight base: 0.5″ ____ 0.75″ ____ Slotted: Across ____ Slotted: Diagonal ____			
Gas cylinder lock			
Gas cylinder lock screw			

Front Sight Assembly

Front sight			
Front sight screw			
Front sight seal			

255

M1 Garand Evaluation Sheet, cont.

	Type	Mgf'r	Replace With	
Stacking Swivel Assembly				
Stacking swivel: Drawing #				
Stock Assembly				
Type				
Ordnance Department Mark:	Crossed Cannons _____	Defense Eagle _____		
"P" Firing proof size _____	Circled ___	Boxed ___	Plain ___	Serifs ____
Cartouche	Yes ___ No ___	Initials _____		
Stock ferrule				
Butt plate				
Front handguard-marked				
Front handguard liner				
Rear handguard				
Rear handguard band				
Lower band				

List of G.I. Accessories with M1 Garand Serial #_____